Frank O. Kelley
1217 Huntoon
Topeka, Kansas

Photo by Thomas Norrell

Replica of the **Lafayette** (see p. 58) as it appeared in the fall of 1955, during the making of a motion picture in northern Georgia. For the picture, which was based on the story of the famous Civil War locomotive **General** (see p. 84), this "One-Armed Billy" of the 1830's was disguised as the **Yonah**, of the Cooper Iron Works Rail Road, and is shown here as it was operating on the Tallulah Falls Railway. *(Color plate contributed by Thomas Norrell.)*

United States National Museum
Bulletin 210

THE FIRST QUARTER-CENTURY OF STEAM LOCOMOTIVES IN NORTH AMERICA

Remaining Relics and Operable Replicas with a Catalog of Locomotive Models in the U. S. National Museum

by SMITH HEMPSTONE OLIVER
Curator of Land Transportation
United States National Museum

SMITHSONIAN INSTITUTION · WASHINGTON, D. C. · 1956

ADVERTISEMENT

The scientific publications of the National Museum include two series known, respectively, as *Proceedings* and *Bulletin.*

The *Proceedings* series, begun in 1878, is intended primarily as a medium for the publication of original papers based on the collections of the National Museum, that set forth newly acquired facts in biology, anthropology, and geology, with descriptions of new forms and revisions of limited groups. Copies of each paper, in pamphlet form, are distributed as published to libraries and scientific organizations and to specialists and others interested in the different subjects. The dates at which these separate papers are published are recorded in the table of contents of each of the volumes.

The series of *Bulletins,* the first of which was issued in 1875, contains separate publications comprising monographs of large zoological groups and other general systematic treatises (occasionally in several volumes), faunal works, reports of expeditions, catalogs of type specimens, special collections, and other material of similar nature. The majority of the volumes are octavo in size, but a quarto size has been adopted in a few instances. In the *Bulletin* series appear volumes under the heading *Contributions from the United States National Herbarium,* in octavo form, published by the National Museum since 1902, which contain papers relating to the botanical collections of the Museum.

The present work forms No. 210 of the *Bulletin* series.

Remington Kellogg,
Director, United States National Museum.

CONTENTS

FOREWORD

The Vanishing Iron Horse

As the midpoint of the 20th century was reached, the curtain was falling upon the final phases of steam locomotive operation in North America. Almost certainly, after another decade there would remain in service comparatively few representatives of the engine which had been the primary source of motive power of the railroads for over a hundred years.

In that comparatively short time the steam locomotive had changed the United States from a small country with a few seaports, and with towns and settlements little farther inland than river navigation permitted, to a great nation covered with cities and spanning a continent. It had made possible the confederation of the isolated provinces of Canada into a great Dominion. Now, by the 1950's, owing to the emergence of another type of motive power, it had become obsolete and its days could be numbered.

No future generation would experience the thrill enjoyed by its predecessors. No future American could stand awed beside the track and behold the majestic onrush of the iron horse, be deafened by the blast of the exhaust, the crash and clatter of steel on steel, and the hiss of escaping steam, or be momentarily shaken as the locomotive thundered past in a blurred flash of connecting rods, valve mechanism, and pounding wheels.

No child at night would ever again awaken to the eerie echo of a far-off steam whistle crying at a lonely crossing, or by day look out from a hillside at the long white plume of steam that marked a distant train charging down the valley below. The present generation of Americans can gaze back upon these things with nostalgia. The next will never know them.

Here and there a steam engine will be saved, but the people of a different era will note them and quickly pass on, wondering. Only a few will pause to marvel and ponder over the development of the steam locomotive.

It is to the everlasting credit of our forebears that some few examples and relics of the early engines have been preserved; and the appearance of this study of them, coming in the final hour of the steam locomotive, is most appropriate. The author has gone to painstaking lengths to find and sift and bring together the most complete record ever compiled of these examples and relics remaining of the earliest of North American railway engines and of working replicas of them.

Students of locomotive and railroad history are familiar with the almost impossible task confronting the researcher who undertakes to trace the history of early engines. The contemporary account is often a will-o'-the-wisp pursued endlessly through the yellowed pages of century-old newspapers and books; the seemingly authentic fragment of fact is found to be faulty just when it seems flawlessly correct; the colorful description of some ephemeral engine of the past just cannot be reconciled with contemporary accounts and finally proves to have been prepared long afterward, replete with the inaccuracies which most unfortunately result from the inroads made by time upon the recollections of the most careful observer.

Through all this confusing maze the author step by step has made his way, the result being a most noteworthy and valuable contribution to the literature of the steam locomotive. To students of its history, to the vast body of railway enthusiasts all over the world, and to those generally interested in the development of mechanical industry and transportation, this work must appeal as unique and one that will be long remembered.

THOMAS NORRELL

July 1955
Silver Spring, Maryland

Remaining Relics and Operable Replicas

BUILDER	NAME	DATE BUILT
Col. John Stevens	none	1825
Robert Stephenson & Co.	*America*	1828
Foster, Rastrick and Co.	*Stourbridge Lion*	1829
Peter Cooper	*Tom Thumb*	1830
Phineas Davis	*York*	1831
The West Point Foundry Association	*Best Friend of Charleston*	1830
The West Point Foundry Association	*DeWitt Clinton*	1831
Robert Stephenson & Co.	*John Bull*	1831
Davis and Gartner	*John Quincy Adams*	1835
Davis and Gartner	*Andrew Jackson*	1836
Davis and Gartner	*John Hancock*	1836
Matthias W. Baldwin	*Pioneer*	1836
H. R. Dunham and Co. (?)	*Mississippi*	about 1836
William Norris	*Lafayette*	1837
Braithwaite, Milner and Co.	*Rocket*	1838
Timothy Hackworth	*Samson*	1838
Builder unknown	*Peoples' Railway No. 3*	about 1842
Holmes Hinkley	*Lion*	1846
New Castle Manufacturing Co., subcontractor to Matthias W. Baldwin	*Memnon*	1848

Representing the First Quarter-Century

Of Steam Locomotives in North America

ALTOGETHER, perhaps a quarter of a million steam locomotives have been built in America. From the first they have been objects of interest to young and old. They have been depicted and photographed untold times, and as a result a wonderfully accurate pictorial record of their construction and appearance has been built up.

The locomotives themselves, however, as they wore out or fell into disuse were usually destroyed for the value of their scrap metal. This process has been greatly hastened in recent years by the trend toward the use of diesel-electric and other types of motive power. Few remain of the busy multitudes of steam locomotives that served so well in building the Nations on this continent. The picturesque and once popular steamer has today become the vanishing iron horse.

It is proposed to deal here only with the relics and replicas of the historic steam locomotives used during the pioneer days of railroading on this continent, in the period 1825–1849. Of these, only 11 have survived in even reasonably complete form. With the remaining parts of several others, they are accounted museum treasures. Full sized operable replicas of 7 other famous early locomotives have been constructed. All these together afford a good idea of the actual construction of the locomotives of long ago.

Not to be included, are the many nonoperable, wooden facsimiles of early locomotives that merely serve to show the general external appearance of the originals they represent. Many such are to be seen in the railroad collection in the Baltimore and Ohio Transportation Museum located at the old Mount Clare station and roundhouse at Baltimore, Md.

Also not to be included are the modern, full sized, operable replicas of Robert Stephenson's famous locomotive *Rocket* of 1829, of which several exist in the United States (one is in the Henry Ford Museum at Dearborn, Mich., another is in the Museum of Science and Industry at Chicago, Ill.). These replicas, built 100 years later by Robert Stephenson & Co., Ltd., of Darlington, England, do not represent a locomotive actually used in North America during the pioneering days of railroading here, and therefore do not fall into the category covered by this work.

Various old models of suggested designs for locomotives would not seem to come within the scope of this publication either, as the full sized versions never came into being. One such example is the model said to have been built by John Fitch, and now exhibited in the Ohio State Archaeological and Historical Society at Columbus, Ohio. As Fitch died in July 1798, the model might, if authenticated as to builder and purpose, be a very early example of an idea along the lines of a steam locomotive.

On the other hand, there is no assurance that the model referred to was intended by its builder to represent a locomotive. It is thought by most historians that the model is that of a proposed power plant for a boat, for Fitch is known to have constructed several successful steamboats a few years before his death.

America's First Rail Locomotive

Col. John Stevens of Hoboken, N. J., had by 1825 long been intrigued with the idea of constructing a steam locomotive, having had considerable success with steam as a method of propulsion on water. In that year he constructed a small experimental 4-wheeled engine, the first rail locomotive to be built in this country. The unflanged wheels were kept on the flat rails by vertical bars that projected down from each corner of the locomotive. These were fitted on their lower ends with horizontal rollers bearing on the inside of the rails.

Equipped with a vertical water-tube boiler, and with its horizontal 1-cylinder power plant geared to a rack located between the two rails, it was built only for demonstration and experimentation. It was often run, however, on a small circular track laid out on the lower lawn of Stevens' estate at Hoboken. This was the first steam railroad in America.

Figure 1.—Original boiler, now in National Museum, of experimental locomotive built in 1825 by Col. John Stevens.

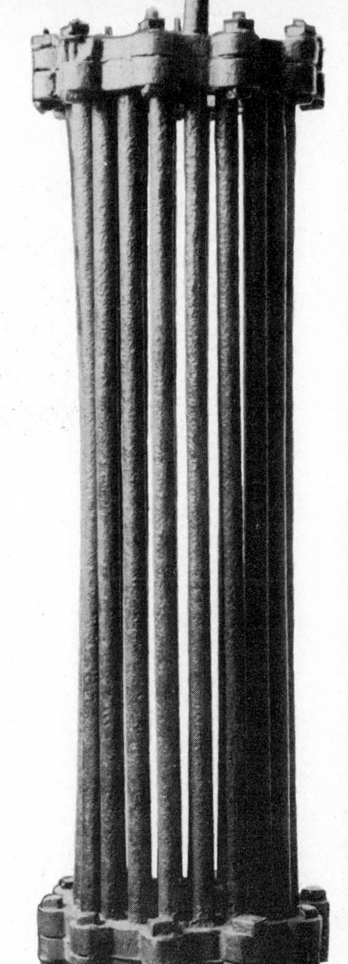

Of this original locomotive only the boiler and safety valve remain. They are on exhibition at the National Museum (USNM 180029), where they were deposited in 1888 by the Stevens Institute of Technology. The boiler (figure 1) contains 20 wrought-iron tubes, each a little over 1 inch in outside diameter, set closely together in a circle and originally surrounding a circular grate, now missing. It is 4 feet high, including the headers, and 1 foot across, and was formerly enclosed by a jacket of thin sheet iron topped by a conical hood on which rested the smokestack.

Wood used as fuel was dropped onto the grate through a door in the hood, and water was put into the boiler through a pipe in the bottom header. Steam was taken from a 1-inch pipe in the top header. The boiler when new is reported to have sustained with safety a steam pressure of 550 pounds per square inch. The design of the boiler was patented by Stevens on April 11, 1803.

The safety valve (figure 2) is of simple design. It consists of a lever 10 inches long from which a 4-pound lead ball about 2½ inches in diameter is suspended. Beneath the lever, and about 1 inch in from the fulcrum, is a disk valve controlled by the weight of the ball, which hangs by a stirrup that can be moved to any of several notches, so that it can be set for different pressures at which the valve will open.

Figure 2.—Original safety valve of Stevens' locomotive, now in National Museum.

A small, nonoperable model of the locomotive, about 2 feet long (figure 3), was made in the National Museum in 1898 (USNM 180241) and is exhibited there. A full sized operable replica, constructed in 1928 at the Altoona shops of the Pennsylvania Railroad Co., was demonstrated (figure 4) at the Stevens Institute of Technology on November 23, 1928, upon the occasion of the inauguration of Harvey N. Davis as president of the Institute. It was given by the Pennsylvania Railroad to the Museum of Science and Industry at Chicago in 1932, where it is now exhibited.

Another replica of the Stevens locomotive, made by the Pennsylvania in 1939, appeared in the railroad pageant at the New York World's Fair in 1939 and 1940, and for a time in 1941 was exhibited at the Pennsylvania Station in New York City. In June 1941 it was placed on exhibition in the museum of Stevens Institute, where it remained until March 1943. At that time it was returned to the Pennsylvania Railroad Co., and has since been stored in their enginehouse at Trenton, N. J.

Figure 3.—Model of Stevens' locomotive, in National Museum. The boiler is shown outside the sheet-metal shell which normally surrounds it.

Figure 4.—Full sized operable replica of Stevens' locomotive, built in 1928 by Pennsylvania Railroad Co., being demonstrated at Hoboken, N. J., on November 23, 1928.

The design of these replicas is based in part on the recollections in the 1880's of the grandson of John Stevens, Dr. Francis B. Stevens, who was a frequent passenger on the original locomotive in 1825 at the age of 11. These recollections are contained in letters from Dr. Stevens to J. Elfreth Watkins, onetime curator of transportation and engineering of the National Museum. Stevens' letters, dated March 30, 1883, January 17, 1888, and November 19, 1892, are now in the archives of the Museum.

Two British-Built Locomotives

The next locomotives known to have been used in this country were the British machines today popularly referred to as the *America* (figure 5) and the *Stourbridge Lion* (figure 6). They were contracted for in England in 1828 by Horatio Allen, who had been sent there for that purpose by the Delaware and Hudson Canal Co., and were delivered at New York City in 1829.

The *America,* built by the already famous British firm of Robert Stephenson & Co., of Newcastle-upon-Tyne, arrived from London on the ship *Columbia* on January 15. The *Stourbridge Lion,* built by Foster, Rastrick and Co., of Stourbridge, arrived from Liverpool on the *John Jay* on May 13. The delivered price of the former was $3,663.30 and of the latter $2,914.90. On July 2 they were shipped up the Hudson River by the steamboat *Congress* to Rondout, N. Y., where they arrived on July 3.

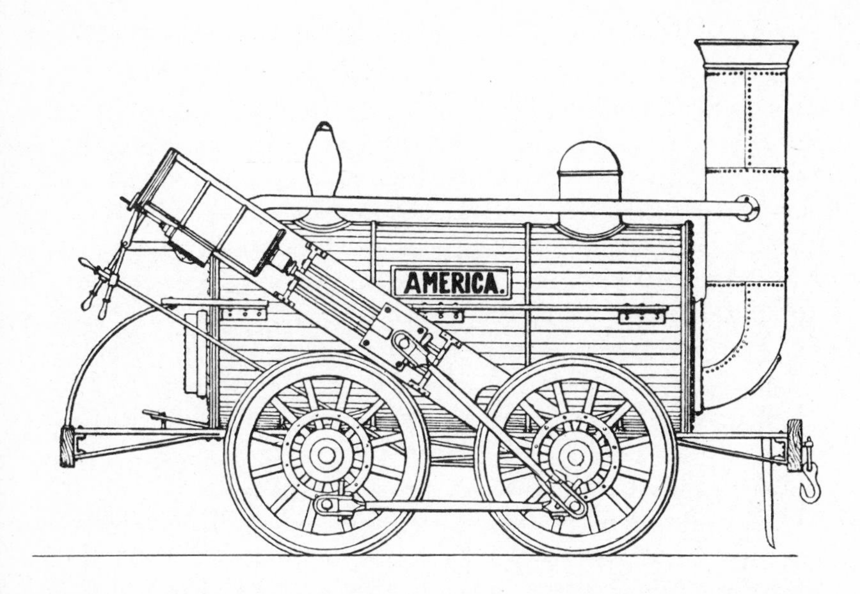

Figure 5.—Early drawing of *America*, built by Stephenson in England in 1828.

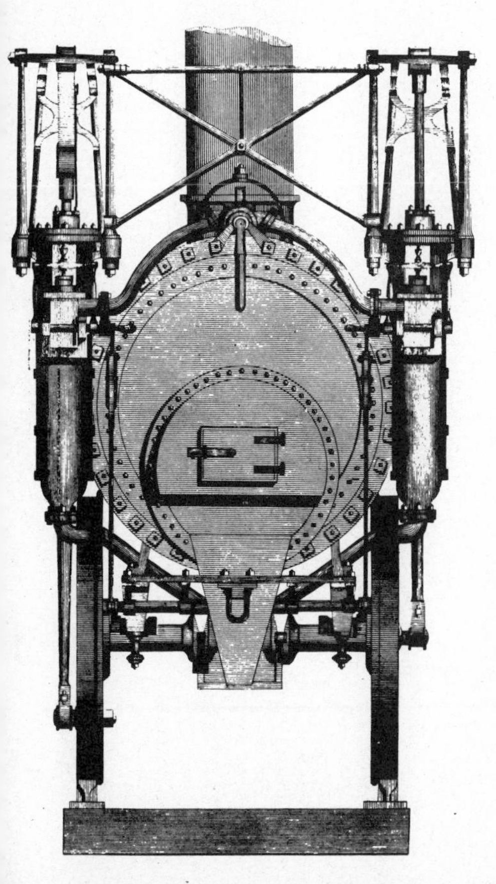

Figure 6.—Drawing of *Stourbridge Lion* of 1829 appearing in Renwick's "Treatise on the Steam Engine," published in 1830 (notice that crank rings are not shown). The track shown is not the type upon which the locomotive ran at Honesdale, Pa.

353689 O -56 -2

Later in July the two locomotives were sent up the Delaware and Hudson Canal from Eddyville, N. Y., to Honesdale, Pa., where the *Stourbridge Lion* was subsequently tried out on the newly laid railroad tracks of the Canal company. The tests on August 8, and again on September 9, with Horatio Allen at the controls, showed that although the performance of the locomotive was satisfactory, the track was not sufficiently stable to withstand the weight of the relatively large machine. As a result of this failure, horses and steam- or water-powered stationary engines (see figure 7) constituted the motive power of this railroad until 1860.

The *Stourbridge Lion,* nevertheless, had earned the distinction of being the first locomotive to operate in America on a railroad built expressly for commercial traffic.

No record exists to show that the *America* was ever used, and its subsequent history as a locomotive is unknown. Two other locomotives were built by Foster, Rastrick and Co. for the Delaware and Hudson Canal Co. As these were not delivered to Rondout until after the *Lion* had demonstrated the inadequacy of the track at Honesdale, they were not sent there, but were instead stored at Rondout, where all trace of them has been lost. It is thought they were destroyed by fire while in storage.

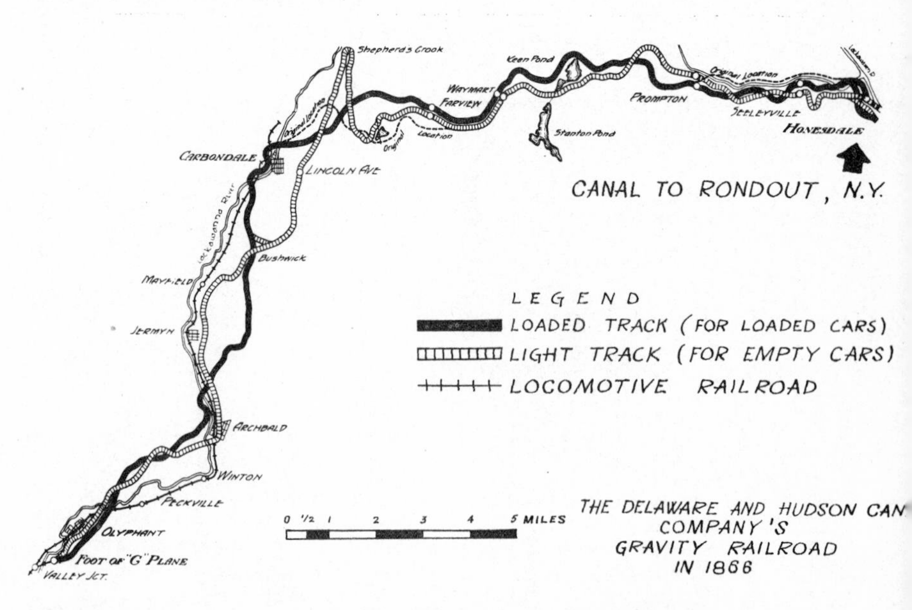

In 1890, Lindsay and Early of Carbondale, Pa., deposited one of the two cylinders (figure 8) of the *America* in the National Museum (USNM 180922). It has a 9-inch bore and a 24-inch stroke, and the piston (figure 9) is fitted with two compression rings. (The location of the other cylinder is today unknown.)

Earlier, in 1888, the Delaware and Hudson Canal Co. had given to the Museum several locomotive parts, all thought to have been from the *Stourbridge Lion*. It has been established, however, through correspondence with E. A. Forward, formerly of the Science Museum, South Kensington, London, and with the firm of Robert Stephenson & Hawthorns, Ltd., that the three crank rings (USNM 180030-c) received at that time are actually relics of the *America*.

igure 7.—Combining different methods of transortation was common practice in the early days f railroading. The Delaware and Hudson as late s 1866, for example, carried coal by rail from e mines of Scranton and Carbondale, Pa., to its anal at Honesdale, Pa., and thence on barges y way of Port Jervis, Ellenville, and Rondout, . Y., to New York City. On some early railroads, orses drew the cars on level stretches, but in illy country where grades were very steep, gravy roads with switchbacks and inclined planes ere often used. The inclined plane consisted of set of rails over which units of the train could e raised or lowered by mechanical means. orses, water power, or a stationary steam enine, often located at the top of the slope, were mong the sources of power.

Figure 8.—Cylinder of *America*, in National Museum.

Figure 9.—Piston from cylinder, at **about twice the scale** of figure 8.

Figure 10.—Walking beams of *Stourbridge Lion*, in National Museum.

Figure 11.—*Stourbridge Lion* partially reassembled from original parts in National Museum. Frame and wheels are not original, and the crank rings are undoubtedly from the *America*.

Other definite relics of the *Lion* received from the Delaware and Hudson Canal Co. in 1888, from Lindsay and Early in 1890, from G. T. Slade in 1901, and from Mrs. Townsend Poore of Scranton, Pa., in 1913, include the boiler, one of the two cylinders, the two 6-foot-long walking beams (figure 10), and the 48-inch-diameter flanged metal tires of the four driving wheels.[1] These parts, with the exception of the walking beams, were many years ago reassembled at the National Museum into a reconstructed version showing somewhat the original appearance of the locomotive (figure 11).

[1] The Museum catalog numbers of these are, respectively, USNM 180149, 209826, 180030-A and 277700, and 180030-B.

Figure 12.—Model of *Stourbridge Lion*, in National Museum.

Figure 13.—Full sized operable replica of *Stourbridge Lion*, built in 1932 by Delaware and Hudson Railroad Corp.

At that time, the three crank rings from the wheels of the *America*, together with a fourth, duplicate ring made at the time of the reassembly, were unwittingly incorporated in the reconstruction. It is this version of the *Stourbridge Lion* that is now on exhibition. The gauge of the reassembly, furthermore, is 56½ inches, while that of the original is recorded as 51 inches.

Also exhibited in the National Museum is a small non-operable model (USNM 215649) of the *Stourbridge Lion* with its tender, together about 2 feet long (figure 12), made by C. R. Luscombe in 1901 and rebuilt by Paul E. Garber in 1920.

Figure 14.—Replica of *Stourbridge Lion* at New York World's Fair, May 20, 1939.

A full sized operable replica (figure 13) was constructed in 1932 by the Delaware and Hudson Railroad Corp. and lent by them to the Wayne County Historical Society at Honesdale, Pa. The cylinder bore of the replica is 8 7/16 inches, the stroke 36 inches. Since the outside dimensions of the original cylinder are approximately those of the replica, its working dimensions are probably also the same.

From time to time the replica has appeared in various railroad pageants, including those at the Chicago World's Fair in 1933 and 1934, the New York World's Fair in 1939 (figure 14) and 1940, and the Chicago Railroad Fair in 1948. Otherwise, it can be seen on exhibition at Honesdale, the scene of the trials of the original *Stourbridge Lion*.

Peter Cooper and Phineas Davis

No original parts remain of one of the best known early locomotives, the *Tom Thumb.* A full sized operable replica (figure 15), however, was made in 1926 by the Baltimore and Ohio Railroad Co. for use in their exhibit that year at the Philadelphia Sesqui-Centennial International Exposition. It has since appeared at the Fair of the Iron Horse, held at Halethorpe, near Baltimore, in the fall of 1927, the Chicago World's Fair in 1933 and 1934, the New York World's Fair in 1939 and 1940, and the Chicago Railroad Fair in 1948 and 1949. Its permanent home is in Baltimore, at the Baltimore and Ohio Transportation Museum.

A small nonoperable model of the *Tom Thumb,* about 2 feet long (figure 16), made in the National Museum in 1890 (USNM 204581), is exhibited in the collection of the Museum. Other small models of it appear in the B & O Museum. One of these, a ¼-inch-scale model recently made under the direction of Lawrence W. Sagle of the B & O Museum, differs somewhat from the usually accepted idea of the *Tom Thumb.*

Notably, the smokestack is not straight, but has an elbow at its upper end, and the belt-driven blower is located there rather than on the floor of the machine as in the replica and the other models. Peter Cooper, the New York engineer and inventor who constructed the original *Tom Thumb* as an experiment in the winter of 1829–1830, mentioned this upper location of the blower in a speech delivered many years later, in 1875, and quoted in Bulletin 73 of the Railway and Locomotive Historical Society (1948, pp. 50–52).

The little locomotive, with its vertical boiler made of rifle barrels, looked rather like the larger locomotive of John Stevens of only several years earlier but had considerably smaller wheels, these being only 30 inches in diameter.

Although a 3¼-inch bore for its vertical 1-cylinder engine is given by most writers, Jonathan Knight, chief engineer of the Baltimore and Ohio, in the fourth annual report of the company (for 1830, p. 35) gives the figure as 3½. Unfortunately, he does not mention the stroke, which is usually given elsewhere as either 14¼ or 14½ inches. The bore and

Figure 15.—Full sized operable replica of Cooper's *Tom Thumb*, built in 1926 by Baltimore and Ohio Railroad Co.

Figure 16.—Model of *Tom Thumb*, in National Museum.

stroke of the replica were made 5 and 27 inches so as to give it sufficient power to operate satisfactorily. For that matter, in the interest of sturdiness and suitable operation the replica is somewhat larger in all respects and considerably heavier than the original. It operates on a steam pressure of 90 pounds per square inch, and it is reported that the original did likewise.

The *Tom Thumb* was engaged in its famous race with the horse-drawn railroad car in the summer of 1830 on a parallel section of the new 13-mile stretch of track between Baltimore and Ellicott's Mills. It covered the 13 miles between the Mount Clare station and Ellicott's Mills in a little over an hour, and the return trip in 57 minutes. The race with the horse-drawn car took place during the return trip. The *Tom Thumb* appeared to be a certain winner until temporary slipping of the belt driving the blower caused the steam pressure to drop and allowed the horse to become the victor.

Nevertheless, the *Tom Thumb* by this and later trips in the same year proved that steam locomotives were practicable, and caused the railroad officials to announce on January 4, 1831, a proposed contest (to be somewhat similar to the famous Rainhill Trials held in October 1829 in England) in which the best locomotive demonstrated would be purchased by the Baltimore and Ohio Rail Road Co. for the sum of $4,000.

The winner of this contest, the *York,* a vertical-boiler locomotive built in early 1831 by Phineas Davis, a former watchmaker of York, Pa., is in the same category as the *Tom Thumb,* not only in that no original parts survive, but also in that a full sized operable replica of it (figure 17) has been constructed. This was built by the Baltimore and Ohio in 1927 for use in the Fair of the Iron Horse. It also appeared at the Chicago World's Fair in 1933 and 1934, after which it was presented to the Museum of Science and Industry at Chicago, where it has since remained.

The original *York* was used successfully on the run between Baltimore and Ellicott's Mills, and subsequently on the much longer run of some 40 miles between Baltimore and the inclined planes at Parr's Ridge, on the way to Frederick Town and Point of Rocks, Md. (Horse power was used to raise the cars at Parr's Ridge in 1832.)

Figure 17.—Full sized operable replica of Davis' *York*, built in 1927 by Baltimore and Ohio Railroad Co.

As the first practical and generally serviceable locomotive of the early Baltimore and Ohio Railroad, the *York* influenced considerably the design of the company's subsequent locomotives. Within a year Davis had constructed several locomotives of a generally similar design, all with vertical boilers (see p. 47).

The *York* had wheels 30 inches in diameter, weighed about 3½ tons, and had a top speed of 30 miles an hour. Not long after its construction, it was drastically altered in design and appearance. The vertical cylinders were removed from the opposite sides of the boiler, where they had operated the four wheels by means of direct-acting rods and trussed side bars, and inclined adjacent cylinders were located behind the boiler, where they operated by means of gearing on the rear axle only.

The modern replica, however, represents the *York* as it was originally designed and constructed. It operates on a steam pressure of 115 pounds per square inch. The original is said to have operated on 100 pounds per square inch, and it burned anthracite coal, a very early use of that fuel in locomotives.

Figure 18.—Early drawing of *Best Friend of Charleston*, built in 1830.

The scene is now shifted to South Carolina and New York. The West Point Foundry Association, situated in New York City, had been the location of a stationary demonstration under steam of the blocked-up *Stourbridge Lion* on May 28, 1829, shortly after it was unloaded from the ship that brought it from Liverpool. The Association soon thereafter built a locomotive (figure 18) for the South-Carolina Canal and Rail-Road Co., which was building a line from Charleston to Hamburg, S. C., just across the Savannah River from Augusta, Ga. Prior to its adoption of the steam locomotive, the railroad had used horses to draw its cars, and had even experimented with a wind-propelled sail car.

The locomotive, the *Best Friend of Charleston,* which was to become the first to operate on a regularly scheduled run in this country, was constructed at a cost of $4,000 in the summer of 1830, and arrived at Charleston on October 23 of that year, on the ship *Niagara.* The same Horatio Allen who had tested the *Stourbridge Lion* for the Delaware and Hudson had become chief engineer of the South-Carolina Canal and Rail-Road Co. and was one of those responsible for the plans of the *Best Friend.*

Local machinists at Charleston were hired to reassemble the locomotive and prepare it for its first trial, but when the run was made on November 2, 1830, the wheels were discovered to be unsatisfactory. They were replaced by sturdier ones, and following a subsequent test on December 9, the locomotive was accepted. After several more experimental runs, some with passengers, the official first run, carrying 141 persons, finally took place on Christmas Day 1830.

Notice of the coming event had been published the previous day, so it became the first steam railroad train run scheduled by "timetable" to be made in the Western Hemisphere. All previous locomotive operations on this side of the Atlantic had been purely experimental—for test or demonstration purposes. At the time of this run the tracks of the railroad extended only about 6 miles out of Charleston, but by October 3, 1833, the full 136 miles to Hamburg had been completed. The South-Carolina Canal and Rail-Road was then the longest continuous railroad in the world (see figure 19).

A description of the *Best Friend* by David Matthew, who in 1830 had been foreman of the West Point Foundry Association, is contained in a letter he wrote in 1859 to the historian William H. Brown. Later quoted by Brown in his "History of the First Locomotives in America," the letter says in part:

> The *Best Friend* was a four-wheel engine, all four wheels drivers. Two inclined cylinders at an angle, working down on a double crank, inside of the frame, with the wheels outside of the frame, each wheel connecting together outside, with outside rods. The wheels were iron hub, wooden spokes and felloes, with iron tire, and iron web and pins in the wheels to connect the outside rods to.
>
> The boiler was a vertical one, in form of an old-fashioned porter-bottle, the furnace at the bottom surrounded with water, and all filled inside full of what we called teats, running out from the sides and top, with alternate stays to support the crown of the furnace; the smoke and gas passing out through the sides at several points, into an outside jacket; which had the chimney on it. The boiler sat on a frame upon four wheels, with the connecting-rods running by it to come into the crankshaft. The cylinders were about six inches in the bore, and sixteen inches' stroke. Wheels about four and a half feet in diameter. The whole machine weighed about four and a half tons.

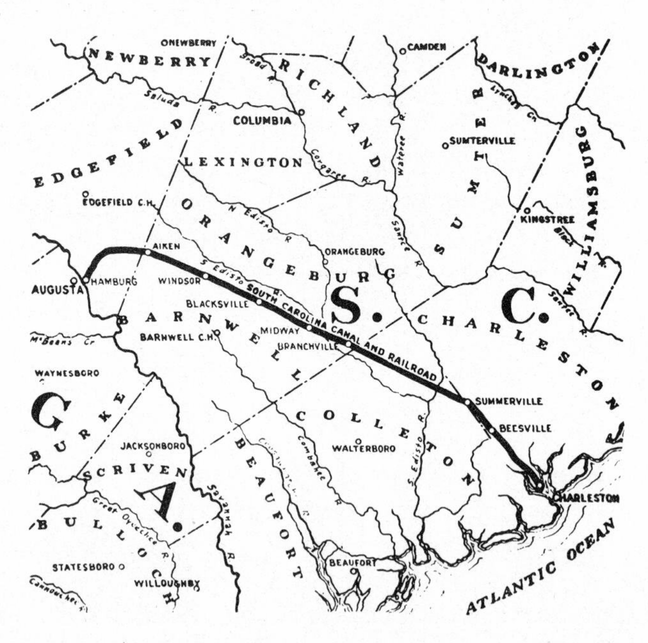

Figure 19.—In 1833 the South-Carolina Canal and Rail-Road was the longest continuous railroad in the world.

Figure 20.—Old locomotive wheel at Redwood Library, Newport, R. I., claimed to be "wheel of first locomotive used on first railroad of any length in America,—Charleston, S. C., to Augusta, Ga., 1835."

The *Best Friend,* as such, was short-lived. It gave service that was entirely satisfactory up to the moment its boiler exploded on June 17, 1831, when one of the helpers on the locomotive deliberately held the safety valve closed.

According to the statement in 1869 of Nicholas W. Darrell, first engineer of the *Best Friend* and later superintendent of machinery of the South-Carolina Canal and Rail-Road, the salvageable parts were used in constructing another locomotive which was appropriately named the *Phoenix.* Darrell's recollection is confirmed by the early reports of the company, which also reveal that the machinery and new boiler were arranged differently on the *Phoenix,* the cylinders being placed outside the frame, and the weight being much more evenly distributed. The *Phoenix* was put in service on October 18, 1832.

Although no documented relics of either of these two locomotives remain, the Redwood Library at Newport, R. I., now exhibits an all-metal wheel (figure 20) claimed to be from the "first locomotive used on first railroad of any length in America. Charleston, S. C., to Augusta, Ga., 1835." Quite probably it is a replacement wheel from the *Phoenix,* for Darrell also stated in 1869 that cast wheels with wrought tires were used to replace the original wooden wheels with iron tires that were on the *Best Friend* when it was salvaged to construct the *Phoenix.*

Figure 21.—Full sized operable replica of *Best Friend* of *Charleston*, built in 1928 by Southern Railway System.

The wheel at Newport is built up of parts, and consists of a large round hub, 12 round 1¼-inch-diameter spokes, a rim approximately 46 inches in diameter and 4½ inches wide, and a flanged tire 4¾ inches wide and about 1 inch thick, the flange of which is 2 inches wide on its outside face. The wheel, therefore, has a diameter of about 48 inches. The spokes are staggered in the hub and appear to be fastened to it by threaded nuts. Four keyways are cut into the hole in the hub. The complete history and exact origin of this wheel, given to the Redwood Library in January 1863 by Isaac P. Hazard of Newport, will probably remain a mystery.

As with other early locomotives, a full sized operable replica of the *Best Friend* has been built. The Southern Railway System, which now includes the old South-Carolina Canal and Rail-Road, in 1928 constructed a faithful replica of the locomotive at its Birmingham, Ala., shops, and in the same year reproduced the original tender and several cars at its shops at Hayne, S. C. (figure 21). A new boiler was installed on the replica in 1948.

Among the various fairs at which it has been exhibited are those held at New York in 1939 and 1940 and in Chicago in 1948 and 1949. At present it is to be seen in the depot of the Chattanooga Station Co. at Chattanooga, Tenn.

A small, nonoperable model of the *Best Friend,* about 2 feet long (figure 22), with tender and two cars, was made in the late 1880's by D. Ballauf, well known model maker of Washington, D. C. It was first exhibited at the Cincinnati Centennial Exposition in 1888, after which it was placed on exhibition in the National Museum (USNM 180244).

Of the *West Point,* the second locomotive built by the West Point Foundry Association, and the second bought by the South-Carolina Canal and Rail-Road Co., no relics or replicas are known to exist. A satisfactory locomotive, it arrived at Charleston on the ship *Lafayette* on February 28, 1831. Its final disposition is no longer known.

Figure 22.—Model of *Best Friend of Charleston,* in National Museum.

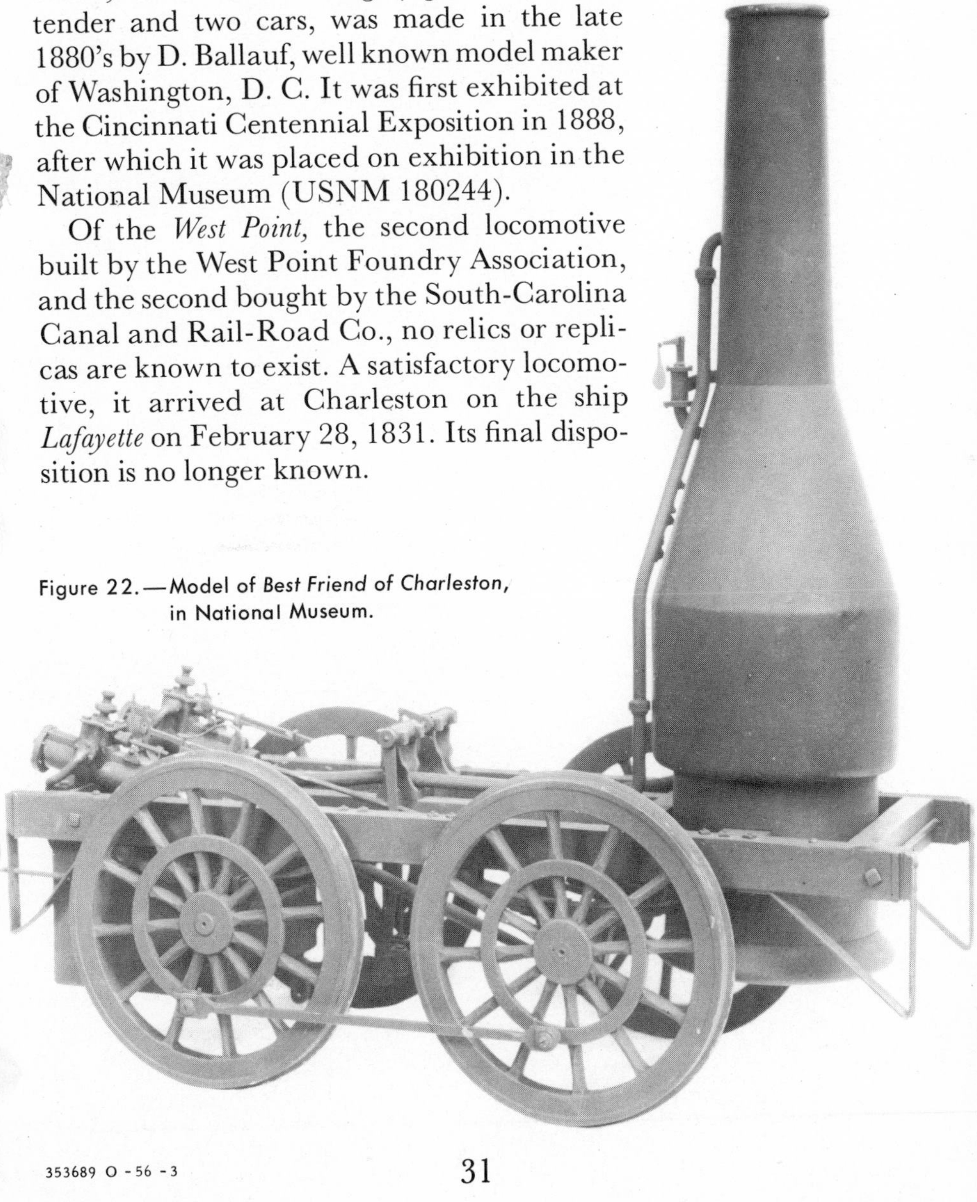

353689 O - 56 - 3

Figure 23.—Early drawing of *De Witt Clinton*, built in 1831.

The third locomotive (figure 23) built by the West Point Foundry Association, the *De Witt Clinton* of the Mohawk and Hudson Rail Road Co., was the first to run in New York State. Its first public demonstration was an excursion trip on August 9, 1831, on a 12-mile stretch of railway between Albany and Schenectady. The distance was covered in less than one hour. Another notable demonstration, attended by many public officials, took place on September 24 of the same year.

The locomotive, which had been shipped up the Hudson River to Albany during the last week of June with David Matthew in charge, weighed a little over 6,750 pounds, was 11½ feet long, and was mounted on four 54-inch wheels, all of which were drivers. The two cylinders, at the rear of the

Figure 24.—Wheel, said to be from original *De Witt Clinton*, in National Museum.

locomotive and connected to the axle of the front wheels, had a bore of 5½ inches and a stroke of 16 inches. The boiler was tubular, with copper tubes about 2½ inches in diameter and 6 feet long. The top speed when pulling a load of about 8 tons was said to have been about 30 miles an hour.

The *De Witt Clinton* was never completely satisfactory, and after infrequent use in 1831 and 1832 it was disassembled and disposed of piece by piece. Some of the parts were listed as sold on April 20, 1835, others on September 13 and October 29, 1836. A total of $485 was realized from the various sales.

In 1891, a wheel said to have been one of the wheels of the original *De Witt Clinton,* was deposited in the National Museum (USNM 180947) by William Buchanan, at that time superintendent of motive power of the New York Central and Hudson River Railroad Co. The all-metal wheel (figure 24) contains 14 round, 1-inch-diameter spokes staggered around the hub, and is 52½ inches in diameter. The flanged metal tire is missing from the rim, which is 4⅛ inches wide, but its presence would undoubtedly bring the overall diameter of the wheel up to 54 inches.

Figure 25.—Full sized operable replica of *De Witt Clinton*, built in 1893 by New York Central and Hudson River Railroad Co., at World's Columbian Exposition, in Chicago, in 1893.

Figure 26.—Replica of *De Witt Clinton* photographed during an appearance in 1921.

This wheel, or an identical one, was used in the very early 1890's by the New York Central and Hudson River Railroad Co. as a guide in their construction of the full sized operable replica of the *De Witt Clinton* locomotive, tender, and cars, first shown at the World's Columbian Exposition at Chicago in 1893 (figure 25). The replica, constructed from the original plans of 1831, was made at the railroad's shops at West Albany, N. Y. During the past 60 years the replica has undergone a number of repair operations, but it remains authentic. It has been exhibited on many occasions (figure 26).

Since the 1893 unveiling of the replica of the train at Chicago, it has been displayed at the Louisiana Purchase Exposition at St. Louis in 1904, the Fair of the Iron Horse (figure 27), the Chicago World's Fair in 1933 and 1934, the New York World's Fair in 1939 and 1940, the Chicago Railroad Fair in 1948 and 1949, and on many other occasions. For years the train was exhibited on a balcony within New York City's Grand Central Terminal, but since 1935 it has been on loan from the New York Central System to the Henry Ford Museum at Dearborn.

An exquisitely made nonoperable model of the *De Witt Clinton,* its tender, and three cars, together about 3 feet long (figure 28), was made in 1932 by Peyton L. Morgan of Lynchburg, Va., and has been since 1935 in the collection of the National Museum (USNM 310961).

Figure 27.—Replica of *De Witt Clinton* at the Fair of the Iron Horse in 1927.

Figure 28.—Model of *De Witt Clinton*, in National Museum.

National Museum's John Bull

Figure 29.—Pre-1900 photo of *John Bull*, oldest complete and operable locomotive in North America, now in National Museum.

Probably the most famous and historic old locomotive in the United States today is the *John Bull,* the oldest complete and operable locomotive in the country (figure 29). Built in England in 1831 by Robert Stephenson & Co. of Newcastle-upon-Tyne, it was officially placed in service on November 12, 1831, at Bordentown, N. J., on the lines of the Camden and Amboy Rail Road and Transportation Co., now a part of the Pennsylvania Railroad Co. In regular service until 1865, the locomotive was given by the Pennsylvania Railroad Co. to the National Museum in 1885 (USNM 180001). It should not be confused with another Stephenson-built locomotive of the same name, built for the Mohawk and Hudson Rail Road Co. at the same time but no longer in existence.

The Camden and Amboy's *John Bull,* its first locomotive, was ordered from Stephenson by Robert L. Stevens of New Jersey, son of the railroad pioneer Col. John Stevens, and president of the company, who had gone to England in October 1830 for this purpose, as well as to purchase iron rails of his design for the track of the new railroad.

The locomotive was completed early in the summer of 1831 and was shipped from Liverpool on the ship *Allegheny*, which sailed for Philadelphia on July 14. It had been disassembled for shipping, as were most of the early locomotives, and it is interesting to note that the freight charge was only £19, or a little under $100. The total cost of the locomotive, incidentally, was £784 7s. 0d., or a little under $4,000.

The engine arrived at Philadelphia about the middle of August, and was then transshipped by sloop to Bordentown, near Trenton, whence a few miles of rail were soon to head northeastward toward South Amboy. The mechanics who assembled the locomotive found it a mysterious and completely unfamiliar device. After considerable experimentation the task was successfully accomplished under the leadership of Isaac Dripps, a local youth who later rose to a position of importance in the Pennsylvania Railroad.

In its first test the locomotive was fired up to 30 pounds steam pressure, and Dripps, with Stevens by his side, opened the throttle of the first locomotive of what was to become part of the Pennsylvania Railroad Co. The engine was disassembled for a few minor modifications shortly after this trial, and a few weeks later, on November 12, the official first trip was made.

The *John Bull* as it appeared when first placed in service in 1831 was described in detail by J. Elfreth Watkins in his "Camden and Amboy Railroad," published in 1891. He wrote:

> The engine originally weighed about ten tons. The boiler was thirteen feet long and three feet six inches in diameter. The cylinders were nine inches by twenty inches. There were four driving wheels four feet six inches in diameter, arranged with outside cranks for connecting parallel rods, but owing to the sharp curves on the road these rods were never used. The driving wheels were made with cast-iron hubs and wooden (locust) spokes and felloes. The tires were of wrought iron, three-quarters of an inch thick, the tread being five inches and the depth of flange one and a-half inches. The gauge was originally five feet from center to center of rails. The boiler was composed of sixty-two flues seven feet six inches long, two inches in diameter; the furnace was three feet seven inches long and three feet two inches high, for burning wood. The steam ports were one and one-eighth inches by six and a-half inches; the exhaust ports one and one-eighth by six and

a-half inches; grate surface, ten feet eight inches; fire-box surface, thirty-six feet; flue surface, two hundred and thirteen feet; weight, without fuel or water, twenty-two thousand four hundred and twenty-five pounds.

After the valves were in gear and the engine in motion, two levers on the engineman's side moved back and forth continuously. When it was necessary to put the locomotive on the turntable, enginemen who were skilled in the handling of the engines first put the valves out of gear by turning the handle down, and then worked the levers by hand, thus moving the valves to the proper position and stopping the engine at the exact point desired.

The reversing gear was a very complicated affair. The two eccentrics were secured to a sleeve or barrel, which fitted loosely on the crank-shaft, between the two cranks, so as to turn freely. A treadle was used to change the position of this loose eccentric sleeve on the shaft of the driving wheel (moving it to the right or left) when it was necessary to reverse. Two carriers were secured firmly to the body of this shaft (one on each side of the eccentrics); one carrier worked the engine ahead, the other back. The small handle on the right side of the boiler was used to lift the eccentric-rod (which passed forward to the rock shaft on the forward part of the engine) off the pin, and thus put the valves out of gear before it was possible to shift the sleeve and reverse the engine.

As no tender came with the locomotive, one was improvised from a four-wheel flat car that had been used on construction work, which was soon equipped to carry water and wood. The water tank consisted of a large whiskey cask which was procured from a Bordentown storekeeper, and this was securely fastened on the center of this four-wheeled car. A hole was bored up through the car into the barrel and into it a piece of two-inch tin pipe was fastened, projecting below the platform of the car. It now became necessary to devise some plan to get the water from the tank to the pump and into the boiler around the turns under the cars, and as a series of rigid sections of pipe was not practicable, young Dripps procured four sections of hose two feet long, which he had made out of shoe leather by a Bordentown shoemaker. These were attached to the pipes and securely fastened by bands of waxed thread. The hogshead was filled with water, a supply of wood for fuel was obtained, and the engine and tender were ready for work.

The distance between the two main axles on the locomotive is just 5 feet, and the gauge is 56½ inches. The overall length of the locomotive, including the pilot, is 25 feet; of the tender, 12 feet.

Watkins has given the cylinder bore as 9 inches, a figure also used by C. F. Dendy Marshall in his "Two Essays in

Figure 30.—Another pre-1900 view of *John Bull*, which was built in England by Stephenson in 1831.

Early Locomotive History," and by J. G. H. Warren in his "A Century of Locomotive Building," both excellent publications. In fact, however, the cylinder bore of the *John Bull* was recently measured and found to be 11 inches. The stroke of 20 inches as cited by all is correct.

Many changes, some minor and some major, were incorporated in the *John Bull* during the next few years. The most noticeable was the addition of a 2-wheeled pilot, suggested in 1832 by Robert L. Stevens to guide the locomotive around the sharp curves common in the tracks of that era. In order to attach the pilot to the front axle, the outside rods and cranks connecting the front and back axles had to be permanently removed, thus reducing the number of drivers from four to two. The *John Bull* has ever since been driven by only the two rear wheels (figure 30). The wheels of the pilot are 29 inches in diameter.

Another early permanent change was the replacement of the wooden-spoked wheels with those of cast iron. The old wooden carriage-type wheels could not stand up under service in America, where sharp curves in the tracks prevailed.

Figure 31.—Original wooden-spoked wheel of *John Bull*, in National Museum.

A wheel, said to be one of the originals (figure 31) but lacking the flanged metal tire, was presented to the National Museum (USNM 181194) by the Pennsylvania Railroad Co. in 1894. An inch or so less in diameter than 54 inches, the wheel would certainly be of the original size if the tire were in place. The 14 spokes and the felloe are of wood. Metal bands, similar to the crank rings of the *America* (now affixed to the reconstructed wheels of the restored *Stourbridge Lion,* see p. 20), are included in the construction of this old wheel of the *John Bull.*

Whether or not it is one of the original wheels applied to the locomotive by Stephenson can not at this time be definitely proved. Possibly it is an early wooden-spoked wheel built and tried by the Camden and Amboy prior to the adoption of the all-metal wheels now on the locomotive. Another similar wheel, until recently located in the Pennsylvania's library in its Suburban Station Building in Philadelphia, is now in storage. These two wheels were included in that railroad's exhibit at the World's Columbian Exposition in 1893.

Among the many other changes to the *John Bull* were the addition of a bell, a whistle, and a headlight, as well as a dial-type steam pressure gauge (figure 32), and the relocation of the axle springs, the water cocks, the safety valve, and the steam dome. At one time a cab was installed at the rear of the locomotive, and an 8-wheeled tender was in use (figure 33).

The tender as seen today is basically original, but much of the woodwork was in such poor repair that it was completely disassembled in 1910 and stored, the rotted pieces of wood being discarded. In 1930 the tender was completely restored at the Altoona shops of the Pennsylvania Railroad Co., and since that time has been exhibited constantly with the locomotive.

Prior to its presentation to the National Museum, the *John Bull* had appeared at the Centennial Exhibition at Philadelphia in 1876, and at the Exposition of Railway Appliances

Figure 32.—*John Bull* on display in National Museum. Note controls and modern steam pressure gauge.

at Chicago in 1883. In early 1893, the locomotive and tender were taken from Washington to New York City, and on April 17 proceeded under steam, pulling two old cars of the period of 1836 (figure 34), to the World's Columbian Exposition at Chicago. It arrived without mishap on April 22 after having covered 912 miles. The locomotive and tender were returned to the Museum in December 1893 after having made daily demonstration runs at the exposition. They returned to Washington under steam via Pittsburgh, Altoona, Harrisburg, and Baltimore. The next time the locomotive left the Museum's confines was for a brief sojourn at the Fair of the Iron Horse in 1927 (figure 35). More recently it appeared at the Chicago World's Fair in 1933 and the New York World's Fair in 1939 and 1940.

In early 1940, a full sized operable replica of the *John Bull* locomotive (figure 36) was made at the Altoona shops of the Pennsylvania Railroad Co. The cylinder dimensions of 11 by 20 inches were apparently known by the shops at that time, as the drawings made then for use in building the replica show the bore and stroke to be 10⅞ by 20 inches. Perhaps the bore of the original locomotive was also 10⅞ inches in 1831, and was increased to 11 inches through many years of wear. However, the figure of 9 inches for the bore, so often used in the past, is definitely incorrect.

Figure 33.—As this early photo shows, the *John Bull* toward the end of its active career had a cab and large smokestack, and an 8-wheeled tender was used.

Figure 34.—*John Bull*, with train of 1836-period cars, en route to World's Columbian Exposition at Chicago in 1893.

Figure 35.—Original *John Bull*, with replica of tender built in 1927, at the Fair of the Iron Horse, October 5, 1927.

Figure 36.—Full sized operable replica of *John Bull*, built in 1940 by Pennsylvania Railroad Co.

Figure 37.—Model of *John Bull* and tender, in National Museum, showing appearance of original 1831 design. Note side rod connecting the two axles.

Earlier, in 1927, a full sized replica of the tender had been constructed at Altoona. This replica of the tender appeared with the original locomotive at the Fair of the Iron Horse in 1927, but since 1930 the restored original tender has always appeared with the original locomotive. In 1940, the replica of the locomotive, accompanied by the replica of the tender, appeared at the New York World's Fair as a moving exhibit, while the original locomotive and tender appeared there as a stationary exhibit. The replica again appeared at the Chicago Railroad Fair in both 1948 and 1949. When not on exhibition, the replica is usually stored at the Pennsylvania's enginehouse at Northumberland, Pa.

A small, nonoperable model of the *John Bull* and its tender (figure 37), with two of the cars of the 1831 period, together about 6½ feet long, was made in the National Museum by C. R. Luscombe about 1900, and is included in the Museum's collection (USNM 233510). The units are represented as the originals appeared in 1831, without the pilot on the locomotive, and without the sides and top on the tender.

Three Grasshoppers

As a result of the success of Phineas Davis' *York* on the Baltimore and Ohio (see p. 24), about 18 more small locomotives with vertical boilers were built for the B & O between 1832 and 1837, the first few by Davis[2] and his partner Israel Gartner,[3] several by Charles Reeder, and the remainder by George Gillingham and Ross Winans. These machines, with their vertical cylinders and their walking beams, earned the name "grasshopper" because of their peculiar appearance when under way.

Of the many "grasshoppers" constructed, three have survived. The earliest, the *John Quincy Adams,* was built in July 1835 and is now exhibited in Carillon Park at Dayton, Ohio, where it has been for several years, the gift of the Baltimore and Ohio. The remaining two, the *Andrew Jackson* and the *John Hancock,* were built in 1836 and are now housed in the B & O Museum at Baltimore.

The history of these three locomotives is somewhat complicated. All were in use at the Mount Clare station in Baltimore as recently as 1892, then serving as switching engines. At that time, with a fourth, the *Martin Van Buren* of 1836, they were retired from active service so they could be modified for the exhibit the B & O was planning for the following year at the World's Columbian Exposition.

As it was the desire of the B & O to show in this exhibit some earlier "grasshoppers," the *Andrew Jackson* (figure 38) was altered to resemble the first "grasshopper" built, Davis' *Atlantic* of 1832 (figure 39); while the *John Quincy Adams* was rebuilt to resemble the *Traveller* (originally named the *Indian Chief*) of 1833.

The *John Hancock,* unaltered, was merely renamed the *Thomas Jefferson* (figure 40), a "grasshopper" of 1835. Why the *John Quincy Adams,* itself built in 1835, was not used for

[2] Davis and Gartner have an earlier claim to engineering fame, for in conjunction with John Elgar they had constructed in York, in 1825, the first American-built vessel with a metal hull, the sheet-iron steamboat *Codorus.*

[3] Although he spelled his name Gartner, and it appears in that form in the early annual reports of the Baltimore and Ohio Rail Road Co., and in all subsequent histories of that road, his tombstone (in lot 34, section H of the Prospect Hill Cemetery in York, Pa.) bears the name in its Anglicized form, Israel Gardner.

353689 O - 56 - 4

this purpose under its original name, is not now understood. (The *Martin Van Buren,* now no longer in existence, was altered considerably at that time to resemble the *Mazeppa,* a so-called "crab" engine of 1838.)

The original *Andrew Jackson,* ever since called the *Atlantic* (figure 41), has appeared at many railroad pageants throughout the East (figure 42); in 1935 and 1936 it was on

Figure 38.—*Andrew Jackson,* bearing number "7," in a photo taken between 1850 and January 1, 1884, at which time it was renumbered "2." Note tender.

Figure 39.—*Andrew Jackson,* as remodeled to resemble *Atlantic,* with Charles B. Chaney at throttle—a photo taken at B & O Mount Clare shops, July 7, 1912. Note wooden barrel used as water tank.

Figure 40.—*John Hancock*, bearing name *Thomas Jefferson*, at the Fair of the Iron Horse, September 30, 1927. When first placed in service, "grasshoppers" did not use metal water tanks.

Figure 41.—Recent photo of so-called *Atlantic*. Note absence of side rod that originally connected the two axles.

Figure 42.—So-called *Atlantic* in 1935, with modern reproductions of the famous Imlay passenger coaches used on B & O in the 1830's.

Figure 43.—So-called *Atlantic* on exhibition in National Museum hall of transportation, in 1935.

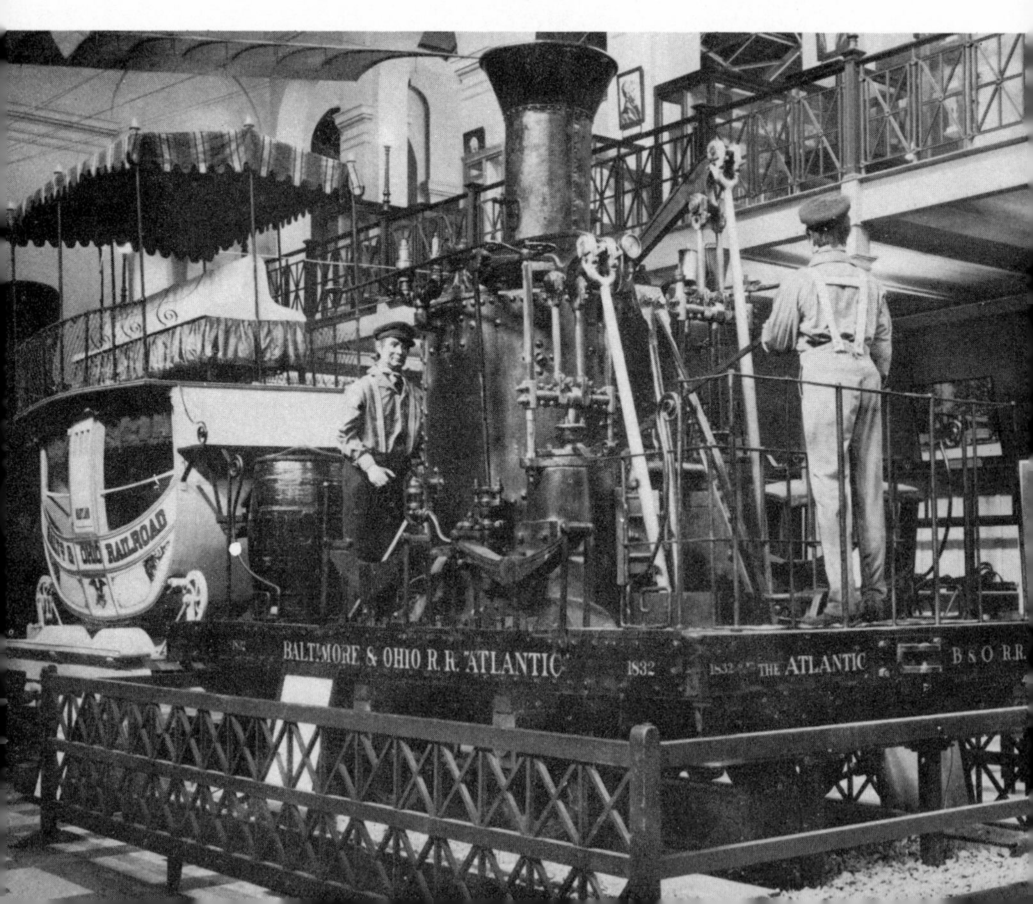

Figure 44.—*John Hancock* photographed during a recent appearance.

Figure 45.—*John Quincy Adams* as restored for exhibition at Dayton, Ohio. This is the oldest complete American-built locomotive in existence. Metal water tank is not original.

exhibit in the National Museum (figure 43). The *John Hancock,* on the other hand, was recently given back its original name (figure 44) after having carried the incorrect appellation *Thomas Jefferson* for about 60 years. Many railroad historians of recent times have apparently not been aware of the name-switching involving these two locomotives, which are now part of the permanent collection in the B & O Museum.

The *John Quincy Adams* (figure 45), recently restored and repainted and no longer referred to as the *Traveller,* is the oldest complete American-built locomotive in existence.

These "grasshoppers" burned anthracite, as did the *York.* The cylinders of the newer two of the survivors have a 22-inch stroke and a 12½-inch bore (according to the 10th annual report of the B & O, for 1836, p. 22) and originally operated on a steam pressure of 50 pounds per square inch. With their thoroughly overhauled boilers, they now operate on 75. The bore of the *John Quincy Adams* is slightly smaller, 12¼ inches (according to the 9th annual report of the B & O, for 1835, p. 24), unless it has been increased by wear or replacement.

The wheelbase of each "grasshopper" is 49 inches, and the weight was originally about 8½ tons. The wheels, modern replacements, are about 34 inches in diameter but the original ones were several inches larger. All four wheels of each are (or were) connected by gearing and rods to the two cylinders. In converting the *Andrew Jackson* to represent the *Atlantic,* however, the side rods were removed so that only its rear wheels now serve as drivers, as did those of the original *Atlantic.*

It is of interest that at least one other "grasshopper" locomotive was built by Gillingham and Winans, but not for the B & O. Named the *Columbus,* this generally little known example was made in 1836 for the Leipzig to Dresden Railroad in Germany, and quite probably was the first American locomotive ever built for export. A description and illustration of it are found in the German publication "Hundert Jahre deutsche Eisenbahnen," published in 1935.

Two Midwestern Locomotives

Among the early locomotives that have survived is the *Pioneer* (figure 46), the first to have steamed out of Chicago, this having occurred on October 25, 1848, at the opening of the Galena and Chicago Union Rail Road. Built early in 1836, the *Pioneer* was the 37th constructed by Matthias W. Baldwin and is the oldest Baldwin locomotive now in existence.

It was originally sold to the Utica and Schenectady Rail Road, in New York's Mohawk Valley, and was their locomotive *No. 7.* Later it was sold to the Michigan Central Railroad, by whom it was reportedly renamed the *Alert,* a name that is open to question. From the latter road the Galena and Chicago Union obtained it in 1848.

In order to get the locomotive to Chicago, it had to be shipped by boat across Lake Michigan from Michigan City, Ind., and hauled by teams to the tracks. The little Baldwin locomotive at this time was given the name *Pioneer.* Its new owner, the Galena and Chicago Union, later, in 1864, was merged into the then 5-year-old Chicago and North Western Railway Co.

Figure 46.—Chicago and North Western's *Pioneer,* built in 1836 and oldest Baldwin locomotive in existence, as repainted for Chicago Railroad Fair of 1948.

Figure 47.—Earliest known photo of *Pioneer*, showing it at work in bridge construction at Rockford, Ill., in 1869.

The *Pioneer* had a full and active life, for it was in operation 12 years prior to its acquisition by the Galena road and 26 years after (figure 47). It was at one time temporarily lent to the new Chicago, Burlington and Quincy line, until that company was able to buy an engine of its own, and was finally retired by the Chicago and North Western in 1874.

The *Pioneer* is a typical Baldwin design of the period. A wood burner, it weighs 10 tons, has slightly inclined cylinders 11 by 18 inches in size, one pair of 54-inch driving wheels at the rear, and a 4-wheeled swiveling truck at the front. The cylinder bore was originally 10 inches, but in 1872 the Chicago and North Western changed it to the present slightly larger dimension.

While owned by the Michigan Central, it had been altered in several ways, the principal change being in the valve motion. The locomotive originally had a single fixed eccentric for each cylinder, with two arms extending backward. These arms were fitted with drop hooks to engage with a pin on a rocker arm that actuated the valve rod. The new motion, installed by the Michigan Central, uses double eccentrics with V-hooks for each cylinder. The cab and the cowcatcher, not applied to the locomotive when it was constructed in 1836, are of a slightly later period according to an article in "Baldwin Locomotives" (vol. 10, No. 2, October 1931, pp. 3, 4).

In common with many of the other surviving old locomotives, the *Pioneer* has been on exhibition at many places, including the Exposition of Railway Appliances at Chicago in 1883, the World's Columbian Exposition held there 10 years later, the Louisiana Purchase Exposition at St. Louis in 1904, the Chicago World's Fair 30 years later, and the Chicago Railroad Fair in 1948 and 1949. At the latter fair it operated under its own power every day each summer, requiring only the replacement of the old boiler flues with new ones of sturdier construction to make it again serviceable. In recent years it has been exhibited at the Museum of Science and Industry at Chicago, but is now stored in that city in one of the shops of the Chicago and North Western.

Not a great deal is known of the early history of the *Mississippi* (figure 48), which is now exhibited at the Museum of Science and Industry at Chicago. Originally it was used on a pioneering railroad operating east out of Natchez in the late 1830's. Some writers have contended that it was imported from England. Others, including Angus Sinclair, the railroad historian, have stated that it was probably built by the New York firm of H. R. Dunham and Co.

Figure 48.—*Mississippi*, probably built in the 1830's, with tender of a later period. Photo may have been taken after locomotive was rebuilt for exhibition at World's Columbian Exposition at Chicago, in 1893.

The *Mississippi,* however, has none of the characteristics of English locomotives of its period, and it is well known that a representative of Dunham took several locomotives from New York to Natchez in late 1836. It is most probable that the *Mississippi* is a Dunham-built locomotive of the middle 1830's.

Its first recorded service began in April 1837, between Natchez and Hamburg, Miss., a distance of about 19 miles. A violent storm lashed Natchez on May 7, 1840, and destroyed considerable railroad property. From this and subsequent financial blows the little railroad shortly succumbed, and the *Mississippi* passed to other owners. Among these were the Grand Gulf and Port Gibson Railroad, the Mississippi Valley and Ship Island Railroad, and the Meridian, Brookhaven and Natchez Railroad. The latter road was acquired in 1891 by the Illinois Central Railroad Co.

In the spring of 1893 the locomotive was rebuilt at the McComb, Miss., shops of the Illinois Central and then was taken under its own power from McComb to Chicago, a distance of 815 miles. There it was exhibited at the World's Columbian Exposition. It has since been seen in many places, including the old Field Museum at Chicago, the Louisiana Purchase Exposition in 1904, the Semicentennial of Wheeling, W. Va., held in June 1913, and the Chicago World's Fair in 1933 and 1934. The tender usually seen with the locomotive and marked "Natchez & Hamburg R. R." is not the original one, but is of a considerably later period.

The *Mississippi* is a wood burner, weighs 7 tons, has wheels 43 inches in diameter, and, according to Sinclair, has cylinders with a bore and stroke of 9½ and 16 inches. Its tractive force is said to be 4,821 pounds.

A One-Armed Billy

Figure 49.—Full sized operable replica of *Lafayette*, built in 1927 by Baltimore and Ohio Railroad Co.

An operable replica (figure 49) of another locomotive of the same period also exists. The *Lafayette,* built in 1837 by William Norris of Philadelphia, was the first Baltimore and Ohio locomotive to have either a horizontal boiler or six wheels. As B & O *No. 13,* with a 4–2–0 wheel arrangement, it represented the first stage of the transition from the old 4-wheeled vertical-boiler types. It was the first of a group of eight ordered from Norris and was placed on the road in April 1837.

According to the railroad historian J. Snowden Bell, these locomotives were known as "one-armed Billys," a term derived from the name of the builder and the single connecting rod on each side. Some of them were in service with light local passenger trains as late as 1857, but by 1839 it had been realized that they could not meet the rapidly increasing requirements of the expanding B & O railroad system. As a result, only the eight "one-armed Billys" were bought by the company, and as early as September 1839 the road introduced on its lines the more advanced 4–4–0, or American-type locomotive—the second stage of transition from the old "grasshoppers" and "crabs."

The replica of the *Lafayette* has one pair of 42-inch driving wheels, and a leading truck with four 29-inch wheels, although the diameters of the wheels of the original were 48 inches and 30 inches, respectively. It looks somewhat like the Chicago and North Western's Baldwin-built *Pioneer,* but whereas it was Baldwin's practice to locate the driving axle behind the firebox, the Norris engine had it located ahead. This feature gave the Norris 4–2–0's greater adhesion and tractive force. The *Lafayette* replica, with a wheelbase of 112¾ inches and a weight of 29,200 pounds, has a tractive force of 2,323 pounds. Its cylinders have a 9-inch bore and an 18-inch stroke, and it operates on a steam pressure of 90 pounds per square inch.

The replica was built in 1927 for the Fair of the Iron Horse and later appeared at the Chicago World's Fair in 1933 and 1934, the New York World's Fair in 1939 and 1940, and the Chicago Railroad Fair in 1948 and 1949. It has also been taken several times to the west coast, where it has been used in the filming of motion pictures. In the fall of 1955 it was used in northern Georgia in a film based on the story of the famous Civil War locomotive *General* (see p. 84).

For many years the replica carried the nameplate *William Galloway,* this name having been given it shortly after it was built, to honor a famous early locomotive engineer of the Baltimore and Ohio. Today, bearing the correct nameplate, the *Lafayette* is usually to be seen at the B & O Museum in Baltimore.

A Rocket in America

Figure 50.—*Rocket*, built in 1838 by Braithwaite of London, England, and used by the Philadelphia and Reading Railroad until 1879. Photo was made about 1900.

The second oldest of the three complete British locomotives of the 1825–1849 period extant in North America is the *Rocket* (figure 50), built in early 1838 for the Philadelphia and Reading Rail Road Co. by Braithwaite[4] of London. It was the first of eight Braithwaite locomotives purchased by that railroad between 1838 and 1841.

[1] The correct name of the builder of the *Rocket*, according to Dendy Marshall, was Braithwaite, Milner and Co. The two brass maker's plates on the opposite sides of the front of the locomotive's boiler read "Braithwaite & Co./ London./ March 1838." However, as they are of the same size and shape as the shop plates of the Philadelphia and Reading in the early 1890's, and as there was no plate on the locomotive in the late 1880's (see figure 51), it is quite likely that these plates are not original with the locomotive. They were probably made and installed at the time it was refurbished for exhibition at Chicago in 1893.

The *Rocket* was the third of the Reading's locomotives, having been preceded by the Baldwin-built *Neversink* in August 1836 and the Winans-built *Delaware* in January 1838. It was delivered at Philadelphia by boat in March 1838, and was then carried up the Schuylkill Canal to the foot of Penn Street in Reading. From there it was hauled by team to the terminus of the Reading-to-Pottstown line at Seventh and Penn Streets, where it participated in the opening of this portion of the road in May 1838. It was first used in passenger service in July 1838, but in 1845, as the need grew for heavier motive power, it was relegated to the Construction and Roadway Department, where it remained in service until 1865. Next used for a short time to move and assort cars at Reading, it was finally transferred to the wharves at Port Richmond, Philadelphia, where it worked until retirement in March 1879, covering during its career some 310,164 miles.

The *Rocket* was constructed as a wood burner, but in 1862 was modified to burn anthracite coal. At that time it was also converted into a tank locomotive, a cab was added, and, it is now thought, the original wheels were replaced by the standard Philadelphia and Reading wheels shown in figure 51. Its present wheels, undoubtedly installed when the loco-

Figure 51.—Photo, taken about 1887, of *Rocket* as it appeared during final stages of its life as P & R locomotive No. 1. Note absence of builder's plate.

motive was refurbished in 1893, are 49½ inches in diameter and contain 20 round metal spokes staggered around the hub. Published descriptions of the *Rocket* refer to 41¾-inch wheels, but this figure probably applies to an earlier set, possibly that installed in 1862. The *Rocket* was formerly driven by all four wheels, but today only the rear two wheels are drivers.

The cylinders of the locomotive, which are inside, have a 10½-inch bore and a 16-inch stroke. The wheelbase is 58 inches and the weight was originally 8.4 tons. This was raised during the 1862 rebuilding to 11.8 tons. The gauge is standard—56½ inches. The present smokestack is not original, and a headlight was not installed until recent years. The tank and cab added in 1862, as well as the bell, were removed at the time of the refurbishment.

After its retirement in 1879, the *Rocket* stood neglected at Reading until it was placed in condition for exhibition and permanent preservation at the time of the World's Columbian Exposition in 1893. It was exhibited in 1904 at St. Louis, and then was housed for many years in the Reading's Columbia Avenue station in Philadelphia. It appeared at the Fair of the Iron Horse in 1927 (figure 52), after which it was taken to the Reading Terminal in Philadelphia. In October 1933 the *Rocket* was lent to The Franklin Institute in Philadelphia, where it has since remained on exhibition.

Figure 52.—*Rocket* at the Fair of the Iron Horse, October 7, 1927. Note shortened smokestack.

A Canadian Relic

Figure 53.—Photo of *Samson*, built in England in 1838 by Hackworth, taken in Nova Scotia by a New Glasgow photographer some time before 1890. Observe chairs provided for engineer.

The third and last of the three complete British locomotives of the 1825–1849 period remaining in North America is also the only extant locomotive of the period on this continent located outside the United States.[5]

The *Samson* (figure 53) was built by Timothy Hackworth at New Shildon, Durham, England, in the summer of 1838,

[5] Railroads are known not to have existed in Mexico prior to 1850, and although locomotives of the 1825–1849 period could possibly have found their way into that country at some later date, none are to be found there today, according to advice from the Mexican National Railways (Ferrocarriles Nacionales de Mexico). Central America falls outside the scope of this work, as do the Islands of the Caribbean. However, a railroad was opened in Cuba in 1837, and another was started across the Isthmus of Panama in 1849 and completed in 1855 (its first locomotive was received soon after the midcentury mark had been passed), so there is the remote possibility that somewhere in this area the remains of a pre-1850 locomotive could exist.

353689 O - 56 - 5

at a cost of about $10,000, for the General Mining Association of Nova Scotia. (Despite statements that the *Albion,* also preserved in Nova Scotia, was built by Hackworth before 1840, it was actually built by Rayne and Burn in Newcastle in 1854.)

The *Samson* was not, as has so often been claimed, the first locomotive in Canada. It had been preceded in 1836 by the Stephenson-built *Dorchester* employed on the Champlain and St. Lawrence Railroad, running between St. Johns and Laprairie, south of Montreal. The *Dorchester* exploded and was demolished near Joliette in 1864. Also antedating the *Samson* was the *Jason C. Pierce,* built in 1837 by William Norris for the same railroad, and destroyed in a fire in about 1890.

The *Samson* was one of three identical Hackworth locomotives built for the General Mining Association, whose railroad was known unofficially as the Albion Mines Railway, and the South Pictou Railroad. Each had an 0-6-0 wheel arrangement, 56½-inch gauge, 48-inch cast iron plate wheels, and vertical cylinders with a bore and stroke of 15¼ and 18 inches. Each weighed 17 tons. The other two, the *John Buddle* and the *Hercules,* were scrapped in 1885 and 1892, respectively.

The *Samson* made a trial run in December 1838, and was put into regular service on September 19, 1839, hauling cars of coal from the Albion mines at Stellarton to the harbor at Pictou, a distance of about 6 miles. According to one early report, a train of 30 coal cars, weighing 3 tons each, was the usual load pulled to the harbor. The *Samson* made about 3 round trips a day at a speed of a little less than 10 miles an

Figure 54.—*Samson* at Chicago in 1883, during Exposition of Railway Appliances. George Davidson, long its engineer, stands at controls on right.

hour. This same report states that up to 1856 the locomotive operated on a steam pressure of 70 pounds per square inch, and thereafter, until it was taken out of service in the early 1880's, on 45 pounds.

The locomotive was operated in an unusual manner. The engineer was stationed at one end, adjacent to the cylinders and driving gear, while the fireman was located at the other end, from which the boiler was fired.

The boiler is about 13 feet long and 4 feet in diameter, and has a large U-shaped return flue. The cylinders are mounted vertically at the rear, and the piston rods are guided by Watt's parallel motion instead of the usual cross heads and slide bars. The engine has no frame, the axle bearings being bolted to brackets riveted to the under side of the boiler. Only the front and middle axle bearings are fitted with springs.

In the course of its working career, the *Samson* traveled considerably. In addition to having been brought across the Atlantic, the old locomotive was brought to Chicago in 1883 for display at the Exposition of Railway Appliances (figure 54). There it was accompanied by George Davidson, long its engineer and said to have come with it to Nova Scotia from England.

Ten years later, in 1893, it was again brought to Chicago, this time to be exhibited at the World's Columbian Exposition. At the conclusion of the exposition the *Samson,* and the *Albion* that had accompanied it, were taken by the Baltimore and Ohio Railroad Co. to Baltimore for preservation there. The B & O later included the *Samson* (and also the *Albion*) in

Figure 55.—*Samson,* with an original passenger car of 1840, at the Fair of the Iron Horse, September 30, 1927.

the exhibition of historic locomotives at the Fair of the Iron Horse in 1927 (figure 55).

In June 1928, when the two old locomotives were given by the B & O to the Province of Nova Scotia, the *Samson* returned to the land of its youth, only to be placed in storage in Halifax. Later, however, it was given to the town of New Glasgow, through which it had run almost daily in its early days, and it is now housed in a small building especially constructed for it at the town's railroad station.

The Final Decade

In 1839 the Philadelphia locomotive building firm of Eastwick and Harrison constructed to the order of Moncure Robinson for the Philadelphia and Reading Rail Road Co. a noteworthy anthracite-burning locomotive, named the *Gowan and Marx* after an English banking firm. This engine during trials on February 20, 1840, turned in what was for the time an outstanding performance. It hauled from Reading to the inclined plane on the Columbia and Philadelphia Rail Road, located several miles from Vine and Broad Streets in Philadelphia, 101 cars of freight, a load of 423 long tons (2,240 pounds). The total weight of this load was 947,520 pounds not including the weight of the engine itself and its tender. The engine, in running order, weighed 24,660 pounds. The story of this remarkable feat is told by Joseph Harrison, Jr., in his book, "The Locomotive Engine, and Philadelphia's Share in Its Early Improvements."

So pleased was the Philadelphia and Reading with this locomotive that the road decided to order more of the same general style. However, as Eastwick and Harrison shortly became involved with plans to construct locomotives in Russia, and contemplated closing their Philadelphia works, most of these additional locomotives were made by other builders. A dozen or so, somewhat similar to the *Gowan and Marx,* were built in the machine shop of a Lowell, Mass., firm named "Proprietors of Locks and Canals on Merrimack River." Others were built by the New Castle Manufacturing Co. at New Castle, Del.

At least two, however, the *Boston* and the *J. E. Thayer,* were built by Eastwick and Harrison, and placed in service on the Philadelphia and Reading in September and October, respectively, of 1842.

What is thought to be one of these now famous locomotives has survived (figure 56). It is the earliest extant 4-4-0, or American type. Known today as the *Peoples' Railway No. 3,* it was obtained at fourth or fifth hand in about 1872 by the Peoples' Railway, which was then establishing a line from the York Street station at Pottsville to Minersville, Pa., a distance of about 4½ miles. Seldom used by the Peoples' Railway after 1883, it was obtained by the Reading Co. in the early 1920's when that road took over some of the rolling stock of the Peoples' Railway. Since October 1933 it has been on loan to The Franklin Institute in Philadelphia, where it is exhibited with the Braithwaite-built *Rocket* of 1838, also owned by the Reading Co.

The *No. 3* has been the subject of much speculation and investigation since it was obtained by the Reading. Its origin and the name of its builder are not definitely known, nor is it absolutely certain for whom it was constructed. Without question, however, it is of the period of the early 1840's, and is similar in appearance to the famous *Gowan and Marx,* although of considerably longer wheelbase.

Paul T. Warner, for many years writer and historian for the Baldwin Locomotive Works, conducted an intensive examination of the *No. 3,* and in January 1934 prepared a thorough paper on his findings, based on a careful comparison of the *No. 3* with contemporary drawings of the various other locomotives, and on a comparison of its dimensions with those still known of the others.

He concluded that from the information at hand it was not possible to state positively which, if any, of these locomotives it was, or even if it had been built for the Philadelphia and Reading. Similar engines, he pointed out, had also been built by Eastwick and Harrison for other railroads in eastern Pennsylvania, among them the Beaver Meadow Rail Road and Coal Co. and the Hazelton (sic) and Lehigh Rail Road. The *No. 3* could easily have been built for one of these roads before falling into the possession of the Peoples' Railway, particularly since it is known to have had a number of prior owners.

It was Warner's opinion, however, that if it had originally been a Philadelphia and Reading engine, it was more likely to have been either the *Boston* or the *J. E. Thayer* of Eastwick and Harrison rather than a locomotive built by another firm, of which the Lowell-built *Conestoga* of 1842 had been considered by some to be the chief possibility.

At first glance the *No. 3* appears much more modern than its actual age, but this is mainly because it has the 4-4-0 wheel arrangement with which people today are more familiar. The cab, not original, is of a design similar to that used on the *Pawnee* class of engines first built at the Reading shops in 1852. Also not original are the headlight, the sandboxes, and the truck wheels. Sandboxes worked from the cab were not used in this country prior to 1846; the truck wheels, 30 inches in diameter, are of cast iron, manufactured by A. Whitney & Sons of Philadelphia, whose wheel foundry was established in 1846. The smokestack has obviously been altered, if not replaced entirely.

The *No. 3,* now an anthracite-burning locomotive, is thought to have been originally a wood burner. The firebox is of the Bury type, which was in common use up to 1850.

The four driving wheels of the *No. 3* are 42½ inches in diameter, the extreme wheelbase is 178 inches, and the distance between the two driving axles is 55½ inches. The inclined cylinders are connected by long rods to the rear drivers. The exact cylinder bore, which had not been known for many years, was measured in October 1954 by representatives of the Reading Co. and found to be 12¾ inches. The stroke is 18 inches.

The type of reversing mechanism designed by Andrew M. Eastwick in 1835 is thought to have been originally applied, and it is also thought that the original steam chests are still on the locomotive. The old valve gear has been replaced by a double-eccentric motion, the two eccentric rods being respectively attached to the top and bottom of a straight link. When the new motion was applied, the old reversing blocks were removed from the steam chests and discarded, the new valves being placed directly on the valve seats. This made it necessary to use only the lower stuffing boxes for the valve rods, and so the upper openings were permanently closed by suitable fittings. There are but two positions for the reverse lever, as was the case with the original valve gear, and the valves are always worked full stroke.

The absence of definitive facts concerning the early history of the *No. 3* is challenging, and it would add much to railroad history if in the near future the complete story could be developed as a result of further study of the locomotive itself, and of the written records.

Of the many hundreds of locomotives built by Holmes Hinkley, the only one extant is the interesting old *Lion* (figure 57), built in 1846 in Boston at the Hinkley and Drury plant. It is not Hinkley's first locomotive, as has often been said, nor is it his first *Lion,* as his 22d locomotive, built in 1844 for the Nashua and Lowell Railroad, also bore that name.

The second *Lion,* now preserved in the Crosby Mechanical Laboratory at the University of Maine at Orono, Maine, was built for the Machiasport Railroad (later called the Whitneyville and Machiasport Railroad) running between the towns of Whitneyville and Machiasport in Maine.

Figure 56.—Controversial *Peoples' Railway No. 3*, built in the 1840's, as it appeared in 1923.

Strictly a lumber road about 7½ miles long, it was abandoned in the early 1890's when lumber became scarce in that region. The *Lion* and a similar but slightly older Hinkley locomotive, the *Tiger,* fell into disuse, and were subsequently sold as junk to Thomas Towle of Portland. What happened to the *Tiger* is today not known, but quite probably it was broken up for scrap.

Alderman E. E. Rounds of Portland succeeded in raising funds to acquire the *Lion* for exhibition in the Fourth of July parade held in Portland in 1898. It then remained in Portland on city property until 1905 when, through the efforts of Alderman Rounds, the President and alumni of the University of Maine, and friends of the University, it was shipped to the University to be preserved as a museum piece. Once on the campus it was stored in various places and received little attention, until it was moved in 1929 to the then newly completed Crosby Mechanical Laboratory.

As the result of a study made in the fall of 1929, some missing parts of the *Lion* were replaced, and it was restored to the point where it can now be operated on compressed air.

Figure 57.—*Lion*, built in 1846 by Holmes Hinkley of Boston, as it appeared in what is probably the Portland, Maine, junkyard from which it was rescued in 1898.

Figure 58.—*Lion* as now exhibited at University of Maine.

Today the locomotive, jacked up so that its four wheels can be made to operate, is a valued relic at the University of Maine (figure 58).

It has been stated that the *Lion* cost $2,700, exclusive of the tender. The bore and stroke of its cylinders are 9¼ inches and 17 inches, respectively, and the diameter of the four wheels is approximately 42½ inches. The gauge is standard, 56½ inches. The locomotive alone weighs 9 tons.

The final survivor of this group of early locomotives is the *Memnon* (figure 59), built for the Baltimore and Ohio in 1848 by the New Castle Manufacturing Co., New Castle, Del., under subcontract to Matthias W. Baldwin. It is one of a small group of similar freight engines built by Baldwin, who won the contract as a result of his bid in reply to a B & O advertisement in the "American Railroad Journal" of October 1847.

The design of the *Memnon* class of locomotives followed closely that of the *Dragon,* a slightly smaller locomotive built by Baldwin in late 1847 and placed on the road in January 1848. All had an 0-8-0 wheel arrangement, and were intended for heavy-duty work with freight trains. The general design of these locomotives had been originated by Baldwin in 1846 in an order of freight engines built by him for the Philadelphia and Reading.

The *Memnon* type of engine had four coupled driving wheels on each side, and early reports give their diameter as 43 inches. Today's measurement of the *Memnon* reveals the diameter of its wheels, undoubtedly replacements, to be only 41 inches. The wheels on the two center axles are unflanged, the better to negotiate curves of limited radius with its wheelbase of 135 inches (in 1847 the shortest curve on the B & O had a 400-foot radius).

The inclined cylinders have a 17-inch bore and a 22-inch stroke, and the valve gear is of the Gooch stationary link type. The *Memnon* is now operated on a steam pressure of 65 pounds per square inch, although it originally operated on 100.

Figure 59.—Recent photo of *Memnon*, built in 1848 by New Castle Manufacturing Co.

Figure 60.—*Memnon* as it appeared shortly after January 1, 1884, when it had been renumbered "13." A few years later it was given back its original number, "57."

The original specifications, as set forth in the B & O advertisement, called for a locomotive weight not to exceed 20 tons (of 2,240 pounds). According to J. Snowden Bell, the weight amounted to about 52,000 pounds at first, but changes reduced it to about 47,000 pounds. It would be interesting to know what parts, unnecessary enough to justify their removal or so sturdy that they could be drastically lightened, were involved in changes that reduced the total weight by 5,000 pounds. Today, the unloaded weight of the engine and tender together is 74,700 pounds. The tractive force is 8,580 pounds. As was true of the Baldwin-built *Pioneer*, the cowcatcher of the *Memnon* was not installed originally.

This class of locomotive, which burned bituminous coal, introduced to the B & O the grate having a rocking bar in the center, with fingers on each side that interlocked with projections on fixed bars in front and behind. The rocking bar operated from the footboard.

The *Memnon* has appeared with other engines in the historic collection of the Baltimore and Ohio Railroad at many expositions, fairs, and railroad pageants. Its permanent home is now that railroad's transportation museum at Baltimore. Originally numbered *57,* the *Memnon* was renumbered *13* on January 1, 1884 (figure 60), and when on exhibition at St. Louis in 1904 it was incorrectly labeled *Dragon.*

Today, however, bearing its correct name and number, it stands on the roster as the oldest of all extant B & O freight locomotives, as well as the last of the locomotives to have survived the first quarter-century of railroading in North America.

Models, in the National Museum, of Locomotives Not Included in This Work

Certain of the locomotives, locomotive parts, and models described in the foregoing pages have been noted as being in the collection of the United States National Museum. In addition to these, the collection of the Museum includes 21 models of locomotives that do not fall into the scope of this work, as the originals they represent are either no longer in existence, are of too recent vintage, or were not used in North America. Among them are five operable models—four steam and one electric.

The originals represented by many of these models were involved in notable events in the history of railroading or mark major steps in its progress. For these reasons, and in order to provide the reader with a complete catalog of the locomotive collection of the United States National Museum, a brief description of each will be given on the pages that follow.

Trevithick Locomotive, 1804

The National Museum's nonoperable model shown in figure 61 represents the probable form of the first rail locomotive of Richard Trevithick, the Cornish engineer who was one of the early advocates of the high-pressure steam engine. The Museum's model (USNM 180058) is about 20 inches in length, and its flywheel is about 10 inches in diameter. It was obtained in 1888 from its builder D. Ballauf, a model maker often employed by the Museum.

Figure 61.—Model of Trevithick locomotive, 1804.

Trevithick, who a few years earlier had constructed several successful steam vehicles for use on the highways, in February 1804 completed the construction of a machine at Pen-y-darran, near Merthyr Tydfil, Glamorganshire, Wales, for use at the Pen-y-darran Iron Works of Samuel Homfray. It is thought to have been the first steam locomotive ever propelled along a railway.

The first trip was made on Monday, February 13, 1804. Among the several trips made by the locomotive was one of 9 miles, between Merthyr Tydfil and Abercynon, drawing 5 cars with a load of 10 tons of iron and 70 men. Although a satisfactory machine, and one that proved that a useful load could be hauled through the adhesion of wheels on smooth track, it was not long in use because of frequent breakage of the primitive railway.

The single horizontal steam cylinder, projecting partly into the end of the boiler, operated a crankshaft fitted with a large-diameter flywheel. The driving wheels were coupled to the crankshaft by gearing. The bore and stroke of the cylinder are said to have been about 8¼ and 54 inches, respectively, and the unflanged wheels were about 45 inches in diameter. Discharge of the exhaust steam into the chimney was utilized with this particular locomotive, as Trevithick appreciated fully the effect it had upon the fire. The date of this early use of exhaust steam to aid the fire greatly antedates those claimed for later locomotive builders.

Trevithick Locomotive Catch-me-who-can, 1808

Trevithick's next best known locomotive, his *Catch-me-who-can,* is represented in the national collection by a 9-inch-long nonoperable model (USNM 244889). The model (figure 62) was transferred to the Museum from the U. S. Department of the Interior in 1906. Nothing further is known of its origin.

The original *Catch-me-who-can,* built for Trevithick by Hazeldine and Rastrick of Bridgnorth, was exhibited in the summer of 1808 in London on a small circular railway laid down on part of the ground now occupied by Euston Square. The public was charged admission to enter a small enclosure to view the demonstration or ride in a small car pulled by the locomotive.

As on his 1804 locomotive, a single cylinder projecting partly within the end of the boiler was used, but it was vertical instead of horizontal. The rear wheels only were driven, actuated by long, return connecting rods attached to the ends of a wide crosshead. Because of the necessary arrangement of the cranks on the ends of the rear axle, it was entirely possible for the engine to stop on dead center. This was likewise a fault of the 1804 locomotive, which had a single crank.

The engine is said to have weighed 8 tons and to have traveled at a speed of 12 miles an hour, but troubles with the track ultimately brought the demonstrations to a halt. No dimensions are known today of the original *Catch-me-who-can,* which has long since disappeared.

Figure 62.—Model of Trevithick *Catch-me-who-can,* 1808.

Stephenson Locomotive Rocket, 1829

Probably the most famous of Robert Stephenson's many locomotives, the *Rocket,* winner of the Rainhill Trials in October 1829, is represented in the Museum collection by a nonoperable model (figure 63) that, with its tender, is a little less than 1½ feet long. The model was transferred to the Museum (USNM 244890) from the U. S. Department of the Interior in 1906.

The original *Rocket,* the considerably altered remains of which now appear on exhibition in the Science Museum at South Kensington, was constructed by Stephenson at Newcastle-upon-Tyne to compete for the £500 prize offered by the Liverpool and Manchester Railway. The *Rocket* turned out to be the only one of the five competing machines to finish the trials. Its success was especially important because it showed beyond doubt that steam locomotives were suitable for general railway work, and also because they could attain speeds not previously known. Running with a light load, it reached a speed of 29 miles an hour.

The locomotive weighed 3¼ tons empty and 4¼ tons in working order. It had two inclined cylinders of 8-inch bore

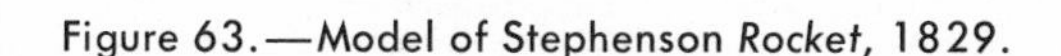

Figure 63.—Model of Stephenson *Rocket,* 1829.

and 17-inch stroke and two 56½-inch-diameter driving wheels at the front. A tubular boiler suggested by Henry Booth, the secretary and treasurer of the Liverpool and Manchester Railway, is said to have contributed greatly to the success of the *Rocket* during the trials. It must not be forgotten, however, that in America John Stevens had used successfully a tubular boiler in his experimental locomotive in 1825.

The *Rocket* was used on the Liverpool and Manchester Railway until 1836, and from then until 1844 on the Midgeholme Railway near Carlisle. It was presented to the Science Museum in 1862, where it is now an outstanding exhibit in the railroad collection.

J. G. H. Warren's history of Robert Stephenson & Co., which contains detailed and well illustrated accounts of the *Rocket* and of the Rainhill Trials, will interest those seeking further details on either subject.

Baldwin Locomotive Old Ironsides, 1832

The locomotive *Old Ironsides* is represented in the Museum's collection by a nonoperable model (figure 64) that, with its tender, is 3 feet long. The model (USNM 180114) was given to the Museum in 1889 by Burnham, Parry, Williams & Co., who were then proprietors of the Baldwin Locomotive Works.

Figure 64.—Model of Baldwin *Old Ironsides*, 1832.

The original *Old Ironsides* was the first full sized locomotive built by Matthias W. Baldwin, a jeweler turned machinist, of Philadelphia. It was constructed for the Philadelphia, Germantown, and Norristown Rail-Road Co., which had been using horse cars in operating a short line of only 6 miles between Philadelphia and Germantown.

The line's first locomotive, *Old Ironsides,* was initially operated on the road on November 23, 1832, and was a success from the start, though a few understandable imperfections were noted during the trials and shortly corrected. The fairly new locomotive *John Bull* of the Camden and Amboy Rail Road and Transportation Co. had been inspected by Baldwin before he undertook the project. Undoubtedly it furnished helpful suggestions to the man whose locomotive building enterprise was ultimately to eclipse anything possibly dreamed of by him.

The locomotive, contracted for at $4,000 but for which Baldwin was, after some difficulty, able to collect only $3,500, was somewhat similar to the locomotives of the English *Planet* class quite popular at the time. The two driving wheels, located at the rear, were larger than the carrying ones at the front, the diameters being 54 and 45 inches, respectively. The two cylinders had a bore of 9½ inches and a stroke of 18. The exhaust steam was discharged into the chimney in order to increase the draft. The boiler, 30 inches in diameter, contained 72 copper tubes 1½ inches in diameter and 7 feet long.

A complete description of *Old Ironsides* and detailed accounts of its first trials are to be found in "History of the Baldwin Locomotive Works, 1831–1923."

Davis and Gartner Locomotive Arabian, 1834

Davis and Gartner, who built the *Atlantic* in 1832 for the Baltimore and Ohio Rail Road (see p. 47), built as their next two "grasshoppers" the *Traveller* and the *Arabian.* The latter of these was placed in service on the B & O in July 1834. Neither of these two locomotives is extant, but a 2-foot-long nonoperable model of the *Arabian* (figure 65) is now in the National Museum collection (USNM 233511). It was made in the Museum in about 1900 by C. R. Luscombe.

The *Arabian* was similar in design to the three "grasshoppers" that have survived, but differed from them in many small ways. Its two cylinders, for example, had a bore and stroke of 12 and 22 inches. This bore was fractionally less than that of the other three. Also, its weight with fuel and water, 7½ tons, was about a ton less than that of any of the others.

The extent to which the Museum's model represents these slight differences between the *Arabian* and the "grasshoppers" that followed it cannot now be determined. Most of these differences would be impossible to reproduce on such a small scale. It is entirely possible that the model represented no particular "grasshopper," and the name *Arabian* may have been selected by chance.

A detailed description of the construction of the *Arabian* and a discussion of its performance characteristics appear in the eighth (1834) and ninth (1835) annual reports of the Baltimore and Ohio Rail Road Co.

Figure 65.—Model of Davis and Gartner *Arabian*, 1834.

Rogers, Ketchum & Grosvenor Locomotive Sandusky, 1837

The *Sandusky,* first locomotive built by the firm of Rogers, Ketchum & Grosvenor of Paterson, N. J., is represented in the Museum's collection by a 2-foot-long nonoperable model (figure 66) of the locomotive and its tender. The model (USNM 180245) was built for the Museum in 1888 by D. Ballauf.

Notice of the firm's intention to produce locomotives was given in the "American Railroad Journal" for December 24, 1836, and the original *Sandusky* was constructed during the following year. Intended for the New Jersey Railroad and Transportation Co., it was built to the gauge of that road—58 inches. However, after a trial trip on October 6 between Paterson and New Brunswick, it was purchased for the Mad River and Lake Erie Railroad by that road's president, J. H. James of Urbana, Ohio.

It was delivered to Sandusky, Ohio, on November 17, at which time not a foot of track had been laid. The engine was used in the construction of the road, which in consequence

Figure 66.—Model of Rogers, Ketchum & Grosvenor *Sandusky,* 1837.

was built to the gauge of the engine. This fact has been given as the reason why the legislature of Ohio at one time passed an act requiring all railroads built in Ohio to be of 58-inch gauge. On April 11, 1838, regular trips for the conveyance of passengers commenced between Bellevue and Sandusky, a distance of 16 miles, and the locomotive *Sandusky* was used.

The *Sandusky* resembled the early Stephenson engines in some respects, but differed principally in having a 4-wheeled leading truck, the wheels of which were 30 inches in diameter. The two driving wheels, made of cast iron and with hollow spokes and rims, were 54 inches in diameter. The crankshaft throws were counterbalanced by a method of balancing devised by Thomas Rogers, who had filed a patent application on it dated July 12, 1837. This consisted of having the part of the wheel rim opposite the crank throw cast solid, while the rest of the rim was hollow.

The driving wheels and the inclined 11- by 16-inch cylinders were inside the frame, whereas the eccentric rods, working off the outer ends of the driving axle, were outside. The bonnet-type smokestack had a deflecting cone in its center and a wire mesh on the top to prevent the escape of sparks.

Rogers, Ketchum & Grosvenor Locomotive General, 1855

The smallest locomotive model in the National Museum (figure 67) is of the wood-burning locomotive *General* that figured so prominently in the famous Civil War locomotive chase of April 12, 1862. (In William Pittenger's "The Great Locomotive Chase" is told the complete story of this epic adventure, which took place when a group of Northern raiders stole the *General* and its train at Big Shanty, Ga. The Confederates finally recaptured the *General* minus the cars, which had been cut loose to delay the pursuers, but with most of the raiders, after a thrilling pursuit that led them 90 miles away, to Ringgold, Ga., just south of Chattanooga, Tenn.)

The Museum's display is constructed from a pair of model kits, to which a great many engineering details have been added. It shows two beautifully made reproductions, scaled 1/8 inch to the foot, passing in opposite directions on a slight curve. Each is 7 inches long. The builder, Adolph H. Schutz of Washington, D. C., in 1955 presented the model to the Museum (USNM 313724), where it had been on exhibit as a loan since 1951.

Built by the Rogers, Ketchum & Grosvenor plant at Paterson, N. J., in 1855, the original *General* was used on the Western and Atlantic Railroad for many years. It is now on permanent exhibit at Chattanooga in the Union Station of the Nashville, Chattanooga & St. Louis Railway. A 4-4-0, or American type, it is the earliest of this particular type represented in the Museum's collection of models.

Figure 67.—Model of Rogers, Ketchum & Grosvenor *General*, 1855.

American-Type Locomotive of about 1890

An operable model (figure 68) in the Museum's collection (USNM 309515), appears to represent a New York Central and Hudson River Railroad 4-4-0 locomotive of the

Figure 68.—Operable model of an American-type locomotive of about 1890.

period of about 1890. This class of locomotive was built by the Schenectady Locomotive Works to the New York Central's design, and had 78-inch driving wheels, cylinders with a bore of 19 inches and a stroke of 24 inches, and weighed 120,000 pounds.

Work on this model was commenced by the donor, the late Robert E. M. Bain, in 1916, and it was completed about three years later, only spare time having been employed in its construction. The model was given to the Museum in 1928. The length of the locomotive and tender is 80 inches, the gauge is 6½ inches, the diameter of the driving wheels is 8⁹⁄₁₆ inches, and the bore and stroke of the cylinders are 1½ and 3 inches, respectively.

The brakes on the model are inoperative, as the actuating cylinders for the brake system are dummies. On the other hand, such parts as the boiler, firebox, steam gauge, water gauge, throttle, and valve motion are all operable, and the donor has asserted that there is even ring packing in the cylinders. Although capable of being fired and steamed up, using coal as the fuel, the locomotive has never been operated.

The number on the locomotive and tender apparently represent the year the donor commenced his work on the model, as there was never a New York Central locomotive of this type bearing that number.

New York Central Locomotive 999, 1893

The Museum's nonoperable model (figure 69) of the famous *999,* long the holder of the world's speed record, was built especially for the Museum's collection (USNM 313161), and was the gift in 1947 of the New York Central System. Constructed by Edwin P. Alexander of Yardley, Pa., it is about 15 inches long with tender and is accompanied by a train of four model cars of the period. Locomotive and cars are built to a scale of ¼ inch to the foot.

Figure 69.—Model of New York Central American-type locomotive 999, 1893.

One of the best known of all locomotives, the New York Central and Hudson River Railroad's *999,* with engineer Charles H. Hogan at the throttle, reached a speed of 112½ miles an hour over a measured mile on May 10, 1893, while pulling the Empire State Express westward between Batavia and Buffalo, N. Y. This was a new world's record, and the *999* was shortly withdrawn from active service and placed on exhibition at the World's Columbian Exposition at Chicago.

At the conclusion of the exposition it was again placed in service with the Empire State Express, but was later withdrawn because, although having great speed with a light train, it lacked the pulling power required for the larger and heavier trains then coming into use. Today, the *999,* altered somewhat, and with smaller driving wheels than when built, is preserved by the New York Central System as one of its historic relics. It is usually to be seen at the Collinwood shops near Cleveland, Ohio, but it still occasionally appears at fairs and expositions.

Designed by the superintendent of motive power, William Buchanan, and constructed at the West Albany shops of the New York Central, the *999* is of the 4-4-0, or American, type and was fitted originally with 86-inch driving wheels. The bore and stroke of the cylinders are 19 and 24 inches, respectively, and a steam pressure of 180 pounds per square inch was used. The fuel was bituminous coal. The extreme wheelbase is 287 inches, and the distance between the two driving axles is 102 inches. The weight of the locomotive is 124,000 pounds, that of the loaded tender is 80,000.

American-Type Locomotive of about 1900

Through the bequest in 1955 of John Semple Clarke, a model (figure 70) formerly lent by him to the Museum has been added to the collection (USNM 314615). A 4-4-0 of exquisite workmanship in brass and steel, the model is 21 inches long and has a gauge of 2½ inches.

It was constructed during the 7-year period from 1907 to 1914 by George Boshart, a toolmaker of Brookline, near Philadelphia, Pa. All rotating and reciprocating parts are operable, though the boiler is apparently not capable of generating steam. There is no tender with the locomotive, none having been built.

It is not definitely known what, if any, original locomotive the model represents, but some of its details are similar to those of locomotives built at the turn of the century by the Schenectady Locomotive Works. While it has been stated that Boshart patterned the model after a Pennsylvania Railroad locomotive with which he was familiar, in certain of its details the model does not appear to justify this claim. The number on the model represents the year in which its construction was started.

Figure 70.—Model of an American-type locomotive of about 1900.

British Locomotive of about 1905

In the national collection is an operable model (figure 71) of a British locomotive of the period of about 1905. Made by the well known English model makers Carson and Co., and given in 1933 to the Museum by Frank A. Wardlaw and Frank A. Wardlaw, Jr., the model (USNM 310584) represents the Caledonian Railway Co. *No. 903,* a 4-6-0 with inside cylinders. The length of the locomotive and the 6-wheeled tender is 45 inches and the gauge is 3¼ inches. A locomotive of similar appearance, though not necessarily identical, is described and illustrated in the British technical journal "Engineering" for August 31, 1906 (p. 299).

The elder Wardlaw stated that the model was built by Carson for Sir Henry Lopes, and that he acquired it from Carson when Sir Henry turned it in on a new one. Wardlaw believed this gasoline-fueled model to have been the first model locomotive ever built with a flash boiler.

A letter from James C. Crebbin in the July 27, 1933, issue of the British journal "The Model Engineer and Practical Electrician," contains the following statement:

> When I was chairman of Messrs. Carson and Co., the late Mr. James Carson and I collaborated in the development of flash steam model locomotives.
>
> With the exception of the very small model L. & N. W. "Experiment" loco which had only one coil, and a methylated vaporising burner, the boilers had longitudinal coils running the full length of the boiler, and were fired by means of a Carson Primus type burner. The pressure container was a drum inside the tender, and was surrounded by water in the usual square or oblong tank. This water fed the geared pump, which was driven from the second tender axle.
>
> The most successful of this type was a ¾-inch-scale 4-4-0 Caledonian, built for Sir Henry Lopes. Mr. Carson always declared that this engine was the fastest he had ever seen, and during tests he carried out, on Sir Henry's track, never dared to give the model more than half-throttle, no matter what load the engine was hauling.
>
> Mr. Wardlaw, of New York, and a "M. E." Exhibition Championship Cup Holder, has a similar locomotive which, I believe, is destined for exhibition in some museum in U. S. A.

Figure 71.—Operable model of a British locomotive of about 1905.

British Locomotive, 1905

An operable model (figure 72) of locomotive *No. 146* of the Ferrocarril Oeste of Argentina was presented to the Museum (USNM 310585) in 1933 by Frank A. Wardlaw and Frank A. Wardlaw, Jr. The 22-inch-long model has a gauge of 2½ inches. Gasoline carried in the tender is used as fuel. The builder is not known.

Figure 72.—Operable model of a British locomotive, 1905.

The original locomotive *No. 146,* a 4-4-4-T type with a cowcatcher and outside cylinders, was built in 1905 by Beyer, Peacock & Co., Ltd., of Manchester, England. The locomotive and tender have a common frame. According to a small plate affixed to the model, the original was the first locomotive to be fitted with "Wardlaw's composite clackvalve." This invention of the elder Wardlaw was installed at Buenos Aires in January 1908, according to the legend on the plate.

British Locomotive Greyhound, 1905

The original *Greyhound* was locomotive *No. 302* of the London and North-Western Railway Co., built in 1905 at the Crewe works of the company. Of the 4-4-0 type, the locomotive had inside cylinders and was the first in Europe to be fitted with "Wardlaw's composite clackvalve." This was done in August 1910.

The model of the locomotive and its 6-wheeled tender (figure 73) is 29 inches long and has a gauge of 2½ inches. It is operable, using gasoline carried in the tender as fuel. The builder is not known.

The donors, Frank A. Wardlaw and Frank A. Wardlaw, Jr., presented the model (USNM 310586) to the Museum in 1933.

Figure 73.—Operable model of British locomotive *Greyhound*, 1905.

Pennsylvania Atlantic-Type Locomotive, 1907

The Atlantic-type steam locomotive is represented in the Museum collection by a nonoperable model (figure 74) lent to the Museum in 1922 by E. Howard Askew of Baltimore, Md. Constructed by the lender, the model (USNM 307949) is 32 inches long and has a gauge of 2¼ inches.

It represents the Pennsylvania Railroad class E3sd *No. 5127,* a 4-4-2 steam locomotive with Walschaert valve gear.

Figure 74.—Model of Pennsylvania Atlantic-type locomotive, 1907.

The original locomotive was built at the railroad's Juniata shops, Altoona, Pa., in August 1907, construction No. 1734. Originally a class E3d locomotive, it was converted to an E3sd in June 1913 by the addition of a superheater in the Wilmington, Del., shops of the road.

In a letter to Askew (Dec. 14, 1922) the chief of motive power of the Pennsylvania System, J. T. Wallis, stated that the cylinders of the original had a bore and stroke of 22 and 26 inches. The drivers were 80 inches in diameter and the boiler carried a steam pressure of 205 pounds. The boiler had a minimum (internal) diameter of 65½ inches, and it contained 170 2-inch flues and 24 5½-inch flues, while the superheater consisted of 96 1½-inch flues. The distance between flue sheets was 180 inches and the total heating surface was 2,571 square feet. The grate was 111 inches long and 72 wide.

The total weight on the drivers was 127,200 pounds, on the engine truck 35,500 pounds, and on the trailer truck 33,900 pounds—or a total of 196,600 pounds in working order. The weight of the tender in working order was 134,000 pounds. The tractive force of the locomotive was 27,409 pounds.

In his letter Wallis also made the following statement to explain the significance of the modification of this class of locomotive:

The Atlantic, or 4-4-2, type locomotive was developed in an effort to retain the desirable features of the American, or 4-4-0, type of locomotive and at the same time to produce a locomotive in answer to the demand for greater power. To do this, the firebox was increased in area by making it considerably wider, so that a greater amount of soft coal could be burned. The diameter of the barrel of the boiler was increased to allow for greater heating surface, which, of course, increased the weight on the drivers.

To make room for the driving wheels without unduly increasing the length of the tubes in the boiler, the driving wheels were moved forward, the main driver being in the rear instead of in front as in the American type locomotive. In order to carry the weight of the firebox, which, with the new driving wheel location, overhangs the rear driver too much to be properly supported, a two-wheel trailer truck was used. This trailer truck, which is fulcrumed a short distance back of the main driver, is so designed that it has lateral motion, and provision is made for ash pan as well as firebox clearance.

By the use of higher steam pressure, larger heating surface and grate area, the use of passenger locomotives of the three-coupled type, with the troubles incident to the use of long parallel rods, was put off for a decade.

General Electric Locomotive, 1926

A detailed and exquisitely made operable model of the New York Central class T–3A electric locomotive *No. 1173,* now *No. 273,* was constructed by W. Howard R. Parsons, and was donated by him in 1952 to the Museum (USNM 314237).

The model (figure 75) is powered by eight electric motors, as is the full sized original, one for each axle, but because of space limitations and power requirements the model's drive is through gears rather than direct. The model operates on 12-volt direct current. Its length is 43 inches and its gauge is 3½ inches.

The New York Central System purchased 10 class T–3A locomotives in late 1926 at a cost of $100,000 each. These supplemented an earlier group of 10 T–1's and 16 T–2's built for the New York Central from 1913 to 1917 at the Erie, Pa., plant of the General Electric Co. Of this total of

Figure 75.—Operable model of General Electric locomotive, 1926.

36 locomotives only one, *No. 270* (formerly *No. 1170*), had been stricken from the records as of December 1954. The remaining 35 still perform routine passenger service between New York and Harmon, and New York and North White Plains. The numbers in the group now run from 247 to 282 (formerly 1147 to 1182), with the exception of the scrapped *No. 270.*

With an operating weight of 292,600 pounds, the locomotives of the T–3A class develop 1,908 horsepower continuously, with a tractive force of 12,750 pounds, and they can develop 2,488 horsepower for 1 hour, with a tractive force of 18,440 pounds. The maximum speed of a T–3A is 75 miles an hour. These locomotives operate on 660-volt direct current, usually obtained from a third rail. The pantographs are used only when crossing certain complicated crossover switches. Each of the eight axles is driven by its individual gearless motor. The overall wheelbase is 46 feet, 5 inches, the overall length 56 feet, 10 inches.

B & O Hudson-Type Locomotive Lord Baltimore, 1935

During the winter of 1936–1937, The Baltimore and Ohio Railroad Co. conducted in conjunction with the magazine "The Model Craftsman" a contest among model builders for the construction of a model of the railroad's Washington-to-

Figure 76.—Model of B & O Hudson-type locomotive *Lord Baltimore*, 1935.

Jersey City lightweight, streamlined train, the "Royal Blue," first placed in operation on June 24, 1935.

The contest, with a first prize of $500, was won by Fletcher G. Speed of New Rochelle, N. Y., and his prize-winning train (figure 76) was presented by the Baltimore and Ohio in 1937 to the National Museum (USNM 311191). The train consists of the Hudson-type, or 4-6-4, steam locomotive *Lord Baltimore* and tender, together 2 feet long, plus five cars. Beautiful in workmanship, and powered with a small electric motor, the model is built to a scale of ¼ inch to the foot.

The original locomotive *Lord Baltimore* was designed by the Baltimore and Ohio, and was constructed at the company's Mount Clare shops in Baltimore. The weight of the locomotive and tender in working order was 527,000 pounds, and the tractive force was 38,000 pounds. The driving wheels were 84 inches in diameter, and the driving wheelbase was 178 inches. The bore and stroke of the cylinders were 20 and 28 inches, respectively, Walschaert valve gear was used, and a steam pressure of 350 pounds per square inch was employed. The fuel was bituminous coal.

On September 11, 1935, an average speed of 59.28 miles an hour was obtained between Washington and Jersey City while pulling a dynamometer car and five other cars. Although designated as *No. 2* when built in 1935, the locomotive was changed to *No. 5340* in 1942. As it was not designed to handle standard weight trains, the locomotive was later removed from service, and after being in storage for several years was scrapped on July 19, 1949.

Lima Northern-Type Locomotive, 1937

A black, red, and orange nonoperable model (figure 77) in the collection represents the Southern Pacific Co. *No. 4410,* the first of the many such streamlined 4-8-4, or Northern-type, steam locomotives built for that line. This model of *No. 4410* and its tender, about 27 inches long, is built to the scale of ¼ inch to the foot. The gift of the Southern Pacific Co. in 1937, it was made early in that year especially for the Museum's collection (USNM 311340).

The first group of this type of streamliner, which was the conception of George McCormick and Frank E. Russell of the Southern Pacific, was completed by the Lima Locomotive Works in January 1937. The first run with one of these streamliners was made on March 21 with the "Coast Daylight" passenger train between San Francisco and Los Angeles.

Of the total of 50 essentially similar locomotives of this streamlined class, the Southern Pacific still had 49 in November 1954, only *No. 4414* having been authorized for scrapping. At that time, these locomotives had averaged approximately 13,000 miles a month since being placed in service, although many had completed over 15,000 miles in particularly productive months. The earlier ones, represented by this model, developed 4,500 horsepower at 55 miles an hour and had a top speed of 90 miles an hour, although 75 was the highest allowable operating speed. They were able to maintain a 9¾-hour schedule between San Francisco and Los Angeles.

Figure 77.—Model of Lima Northern-type locomotive, 1937.

The locomotive and tender are 108 feet long, and weigh 835,000 pounds in operating condition. The fuel is bunker type C oil. A boiler pressure of 250 pounds per square inch is employed. The cylinder bore is 27 inches, the stroke 30. The eight drivers are 73 inches in diameter, and the driving wheelbase is 20 feet. The later streamlined 4-8-4's of the Southern Pacific develop 5,500 horsepower at 55 miles an hour, and operate on a boiler pressure of 300 pounds per square inch.

General Electric Locomotive, 1938

A nonoperable model (figure 78) of the first of six 2–C+C–2 streamlined electric locomotives built by the General Electric Co. for The New York, New Haven and Hartford Railroad Co. was made especially for the Museum collection (USNM 311880) by the builder of these locomotives. The model, constructed in the Bridgeport, Conn., plant of the General Electric Co. and presented to the Museum in 1940, is of plaster painted green and black, with gold trim. It is 31 inches long and has a gauge of 1¾ inches.

The electric locomotives represented by this model were built in 1938 at the Erie, Pa., plant of the General Electric Co. for passenger service between New Haven and New York. Originally numbered from 0361 to 0366, they are now numbered from 360 to 365.

Figure 78.—Model of General Electric locomotive, 1938.

On the New Haven tracks these 77-foot-long locomotives operate on 11,000-volt, single-phase, 25-cycle, alternating current obtained from an overhead trolley system. On the New York Central tracks they operate on 660-volt direct current obtained usually from a third rail, but occasionally from an overhead supply at some crossover switches. For this latter purpose a small auxiliary pantograph is used. Control equipment is, of course, provided for both types of power supply.

The fully loaded weight is 433,200 pounds, of which 272,400 pounds is on the twelve 56-inch drivers. While operating on alternating current, the continuous tractive force is 24,100 pounds, and the continuously available horespower 3,600. The maximum available horsepower from the six twin-armature, 12-pole motors is 7,600. Slightly different results are obtained while operating on direct current. The maximum safe speed is 93 miles an hour.

American Locomotive Co. Hudson-Type Locomotive, 1938

Development of the original Hudson-type locomotives began in 1926 when the New York Central System decided it needed a new type of passenger locomotive to meet the demands of high-speed, long-distance runs. The type was named after the river along which it would run. In late 1937 and in 1938, 50 Hudsons of an improved design, built by the American Locomotive Co., were placed on the New York Central. These locomotives, Nos. 5405 to 5454, had larger boilers than their predecessors, had greater tractive force, and were fitted with roller bearings. In addition, Nos. 5445 to 5454 were streamlined.

A nonoperable model (figure 79) in the Museum collection (USNM 313162), gift of the New York Central System in 1947, represents *No. 5429.* The model locomotive and tender are 2 feet long and are accompanied by a train of six streamlined cars. The entire train is painted silver, with black trimming on the locomotive and tender. Built to a scale of ¼ inch to the foot, it was especially made for the

Figure 79.—Model of American Locomotive Co. Hudson-type locomotive, 1938.

Museum, the builder being Edwin P. Alexander of Yardley, Pa.

The original *No. 5429,* constructed in 1938, was streamlined in 1941 in the West Albany shops of the New York Central, and in December of that year was placed back in service on the Empire State Express with an entirely new streamlined train of specially designed stainless-steel cars. When the Empire State Express was ultimately dieselized in 1945, *No. 5429* was put to other uses, and the streamlining was removed in 1950. As of October 1955 it was still in service.

In streamlined condition, as represented by the model, the locomotive and tender together weighed 681,900 pounds and their length was a few inches over 97 feet. The diameter of the driving wheels was 79 inches, the bore and stroke of the cylinders were 22½ and 29 inches, respectively, and the total tractive force was 53,960 pounds. A steam pressure of 265 pounds per square inch was used.

Baldwin-Westinghouse Geared Steam-Turbine Locomotive, 1944

A radical departure from the usual design for a coal-burning steam locomotive, and the first of its type built in this country, was the noncondensing geared steam-turbine locomotive built jointly by The Baldwin Locomotive Works and the Westinghouse Electric and Manufacturing Co. Constructed in 1944 at Baldwin's Eddystone plant (Westinghouse manufactured the turbines and gears), it was designated Pennsylvania Railroad Co. class S–2 locomotive *No. 6200.*

This locomotive, combining the work of two pioneers in the railroad equipment field, is represented in the Museum collection by a nonoperable model (figure 80) made especially for the Museum (USNM 312935) and presented to it by The Baldwin Locomotive Works early in 1946. The locomotive and tender, together 30 inches long, were built to a scale of ¼ inch to the foot by Minton Cronkhite of Pasadena, Calif.

Two steam turbines, similar to the type that drive the larger fighting ships of the U.S. Navy, powered the original locomotive. The more complex and powerful of the two, the forward-drive turbine, developed a maximum of 7,250 horsepower and was at all times engaged with the wheels. (Although 6,500 horsepower has usually been the quoted figure for the forward-drive turbine, 7,250 was actually developed on October 22, 1946, at the Altoona Locomotive Testing Plant.) The simpler one, for reverse only, developed 1,500 horsepower and was normally disengaged from the driving wheels except while actually being used.

The boiler, frame, trucks, and driving wheels were of the conventional type, the most notable visible difference between the locomotive and those of other types being the absence of cylinders, valve motion, and their accompanying parts. Because of the elimination of piston rods and other reciprocating parts it was possible to balance almost perfectly the driving wheels, thus permitting a higher operating speed than normally practical with a conventional locomotive.

The weight of the locomotive alone was 580,000 pounds, and its forward tractive force was 70,500 pounds. A 6-8-6 wheel arrangement was employed, the driving wheel diameter was 68 inches, and a speed of 100 miles an hour was possible. The working steam pressure was 310 pounds per square inch. Bituminous coal served as the fuel. A detailed and well illustrated description of this locomotive appears in the magazine "Baldwin" (for the fourth quarter of 1944).

The locomotive covered 103,050 miles in passenger service,

Figure 80.—Model of Baldwin-Westinghouse geared steam-turbine locomotive, 1944.

and was then set aside on June 11, 1949, because it was in need of repairs to the firebox and flues, and also to the turbines, oil pumps, and gears. At that time all passenger service on the Pennsylvania was being changed to diesel-electric operation, so the locomotive was ultimately scrapped on May 29, 1952.

General Motors Diesel-Electric Locomotive, 1945

A nonoperable model of a diesel-electric locomotive (figure 81) was given to the Museum (USNM 313163) by the New York Central System in 1947. This gray and black model, which is 33 inches long and is built to a scale of ¼ inch to the foot, represents the General Motors 2-unit diesel-electric *No. 4000–4001* of the New York Central, a type placed in service with the Empire State Express in 1945 to replace the Hudson-type steam locomotives described on page 99. The model was especially built for the Museum's collection, the builder being Edwin P. Alexander of Yardley, Pa.

The overall length of the two full sized units is just over 140 feet and their combined weight is 646,000 pounds. Each end of each unit is supported by a 6-wheeled truck, and the wheel diameter is 36 inches throughout.

Each unit is equipped with two General Motors 12-cylinder V-type 2-cycle diesel engines having a bore of 8½ inches and a stroke of 10 inches, and developing 1,000 horsepower at 800 revolutions per minute, a total of 4,000 horsepower for the two units combined. Each engine is directly coupled to a generator that supplies direct current to the two traction motors, geared, respectively, to the front and rear axles of its corresponding truck. No power is applied to the center axle, which is for weight distribution only. The joint tractive force of the two units is 108,950 pounds.

Figure 81.—Model of General Motors diesel-electric locomotive, 1945.

PICTURE CREDITS

Figure

1.—Museum photo 25370
2.—Museum photo 2720
3.—Museum photo 23554
4.—Museum photo 43102
5.—Museum photo 43130
6.—Museum photo 16534
7.—Museum photo 43586-B
8.—Museum photo 16048
9.—Museum photo 31975
10.—Museum photo 43076-B
11.—Museum photo 43076
12.—Museum photo 30571-A
13.—Museum photo 32367-E
14.—Museum Chaney photo 24478
15.—Photo courtesy Baltimore and Ohio Railroad Co.
16.—Museum photo 43054-A
17.—Photo courtesy Baltimore and Ohio Railroad Co.
18.—Museum photo 13225-B
19.—Museum photo 43586
20.—Photo courtesy Redwood Library
21.—Photo courtesy Southern Railway System
22.—Museum photo 43054
23.—Museum photo 25012-B
24.—Museum photo 43076-A
25.—Museum photo 43060
26-27.—Photos from Chaney collection
28.—Museum photo 31959-A
29.—Museum photo 14293
30.—Museum photo 34328
31.—Museum photo 29759-A
32.—Museum photo 16538
33.—Museum Chaney photo 8810
34.—Museum photo 21243-C
35.—Museum Chaney photo 13758
36.—Photo courtesy Pennsylvania Railroad Co.
37.—Museum photo 23552
38.—Museum Chaney photo 1429
39.—Museum Chaney photo 1457
40.—Museum Chaney photo 13528

Figure

41.—Photo courtesy Baltimore and Ohio Railroad Co.
42.—Museum photo 32097-A
43-45.—Photos courtesy Baltimore and Ohio Railroad Co.
46-47.—Photos courtesy Chicago and North Western Railway System
48.—Museum Chaney photo 20295
49.—Photo courtesy Baltimore and Ohio Railroad Co.
50.—Museum photo 43094
51.—Museum photo 43182
52.—Museum Chaney photo 13799
53.—Museum photo 43083
54.—Museum photo 30457
55.—Museum Chaney photo 13538
56.—Photo courtesy Reading Co.
57-58.—Photos courtesy University of Maine
59.—Photo courtesy Baltimore and Ohio Railroad Co.
60.—Museum Chaney photo 10314
61.—Museum photo 26977-B
62.—Museum photo 30397
63.—Museum photo 43299
64.—Museum photo 26981-B
65.—Museum photo 26974-A
66.—Museum photo 26899-A
67.—Museum photo 43598
68.—Museum photo 43299-E
69.—Museum photo 43297
70.—Museum photo 26847-H
71.—Museum photo 43298
72.—Museum photo 43298-A
73.—Museum photo 43298-B
74.—Museum photo 43299-A
75.—Museum photo 42272
76.—Museum photo 43299-B
77.—Museum photo 43299-C
78.—Museum photo 43299-D
79.—Museum photo 43297-A
80.—Museum photo 43293
81.—Museum photo 43297-B

ACKNOWLEDGMENTS

The author wishes to express his appreciation for the help given him by the many individuals, including railroad officials, librarians, and museum curators, who provided answers to many questions and confirmed many conjectures.

Special thanks are tendered A. B. Lawson and Lawrence W. Sagle of The Baltimore and Ohio Railroad Co., F. V. Koval of the Chicago and North Western Railway System, W. F. Kascal and Harry B. Spurrier of the New York Central System, H. T. Cover of the Pennsylvania Railroad Co., Harry E. Hammer of the Reading Co., K. C. Ingram of the Southern Pacific Co., Elizabeth O. Cullen of the Association of American Railroads, D. M. MacMaster of the Museum of Science and Industry at Chicago, H. D. Watson of the University of Maine, George M. Hart of George School in Bucks County, Pa., and Robert R. Brown of Lachine, Quebec—to name a few of those whose contributions have helped bring together the facts here presented.

It is fitting also at this time to refer to the late Charles B. Chaney, who collected over a period of almost 60 years an immense number of photographs, negatives, drawings, lithographs, and books dealing with railroading. Upon his death in 1948, he left this entire collection to the United States National Museum, of the Smithsonian Institution, confident that in the Museum it would be put to the widest possible use and would, therefore, carry forward his lifelong work of research in the history of locomotives and railroads.

His confidence was well founded. The Chaney collection of railroad material has been an invaluable source of information for the present work.

To acknowledge the contribution of Thomas Norrell of Silver Spring, Md., is likewise a pleasure. He graciously consented to read the manuscript of this work, and his authoritative comments have greatly enhanced its comprehensiveness and accuracy.

BIBLIOGRAPHY

AUSTIN, ERASTUS LONG, and HAUSER, ODELL
1929. The Sesqui-Centennial International Exposition. Current Publications, Inc., Philadelphia.

[BALDWIN LOCOMOTIVE WORKS]
1922 et seq. *Baldwin Locomotives.* (*Baldwin* with first issue of 1944.) Philadelphia.
1923. History of the Baldwin Locomotive Works, 1831–1923. Printed by the Bingham Co., Philadelphia.

[BALTIMORE AND OHIO RAIL ROAD CO.]
1827 et seq. Baltimore and Ohio Rail Road Company annual reports. Baltimore.

BELL, J. SNOWDEN
1912. The early motive power of the Baltimore and Ohio Railroad. Angus Sinclair Co., New York.

BROWN, WILLIAM H.
1871. The history of the first locomotives in America. D. Appleton and Co., New York. (A second, revised, edition appeared in 1874.)

BURGESS, GEORGE H., and KENNEDY, MILES C.
1949. Centennial history of the Pennsylvania Railroad Company. The Pennsylvania Railroad Co., Philadelphia.

[DELAWARE AND HUDSON CO.]
1925. A century of progress—History of the Delaware and Hudson Company, 1823–1923. Printed by J. B. Lyon Co , Albany, N. Y.

DENDY MARSHALL, C. F.
1928. Two essays in early locomotive history. The Locomotive Publishing Co., Ltd., London.

DERRICK, SAMUEL MELANCHTHON
1930. Centennial history of South Carolina Railroad. The State Co., Columbia, S. C.

FORNEY, M. N.
1886. Locomotives and locomotive building, being a brief sketch of the growth of the railroad system and of the various improvements in locomotive building in America together with a history of the origin and growth of the Rogers Locomotive and Machine Works, Paterson, New Jersey, from 1831 to 1886. Printed by Wm. S. Gottsberger, New York.

[GERMAN STATE RAILWAYS]
1935. Hundert Jahre deutsche Eisenbahnen. Germany.

HARRISON, JOSEPH, Jr.
1872. The locomotive engine, and Philadelphia's share in its early improvements. George Gebbie, Philadelphia.

Hinchman, Walter S.
1913. Holmes Hinkley, an industrial pioneer, 1793–1866. Riverside Press, Cambridge, Mass.

Hungerford, Edward
1928. The story of the Baltimore & Ohio Railroad, 1827–1927. G. P. Putnam's Sons, New York.
1938. Men and iron—The history of New York Central. Thomas Y. Crowell Co., New York.

[Pennsylvania Railroad Co.]
1893. Catalogue of the exhibit of the Pennsylvania Railroad Company at the World's Columbian Exposition. Chicago.

Pittenger, William
1893. The Great Locomotive Chase. Jones and Stanley, New York.

[Railway and Locomotive Historical Society]
1921 et seq. Railway and Locomotive Historical Society bulletins. Boston, Mass.

Renwick, James
1830. Treatise on the steam engine. G. & C. & H. Carvill, New York.

Sagle, Lawrence W.
1952. A picture history of B & O motive power. Simmons-Boardman Publishing Corp., New York.

Sinclair, Angus
1907. Development of the locomotive engine. D. Van Nostrand Co., New York.

Stevens, Frank Walker
1926. The beginnings of the New York Central Railroad—A history. G. P. Putnam's Sons, New York.

Warner, Paul T.
1934. Locomotive Number 3, Peoples' Railway. Unpublished manuscript in the files of The Franklin Institute, Philadelphia.

Warren, J. G. H.
1923. A century of locomotive building by Robert Stephenson & Co., 1823–1923. Andrew Reid & Co., Ltd., Newcastle-upon-Tyne.

Watkins, J. Elfreth
1891. The Camden and Amboy Railroad—Origin and Early History, an address appearing in Ceremonies upon the completion of the monument erected by the Pennsylvania Railroad Company at Bordentown, New Jersey, to mark the first piece of track laid between New York and Philadelphia in 1831. William F. Roberts, Washington, D. C.

Young, Robert
1923. Timothy Hackworth and the locomotive. The Locomotive Publishing Co., Ltd., London.

INDEX

For sale by the Superintendent of Documents, U. S. Government Printing Office
Washington 25, D. C. - Price $1.00

U. S. GOVERNMENT PRINTING OFFICE: 1956 O-F—353689